Don't Mess with Science

BY ANNA CLAYBOURNE

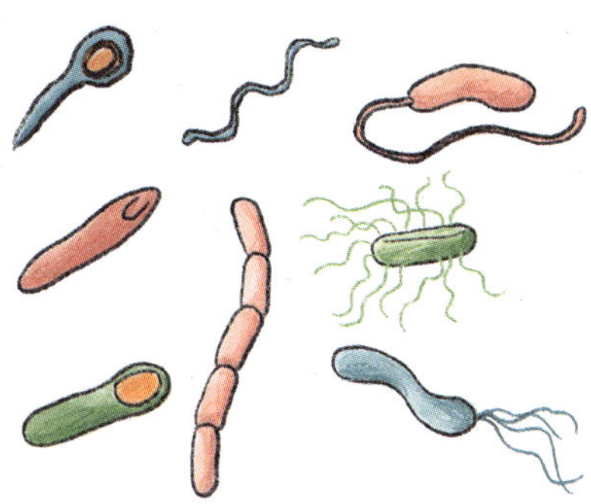

ARCTURUS

ARCTURUS

This edition published in 2023 by Arcturus Publishing Limited
26/27 Bickels Yard, 151–153 Bermondsey Street,
London SE1 3HA

Author: Anna Claybourne
Illustrator: Shanarama
Designer: Jeni Child
Editor: Violet Peto
Design Manager: Jessica Holliland
Editorial Manager: Joe Harris

Published and Distributed in India by Scholastic India Pvt. Ltd.
This reprint edition: February, 2025

ISBN: 978-93-5954-500-4

Printed in India

Contents

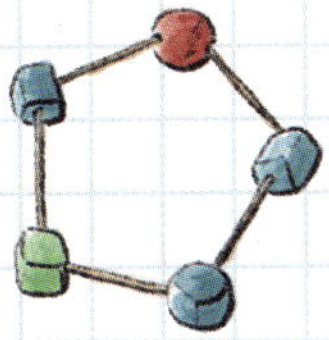

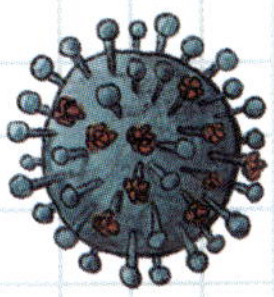

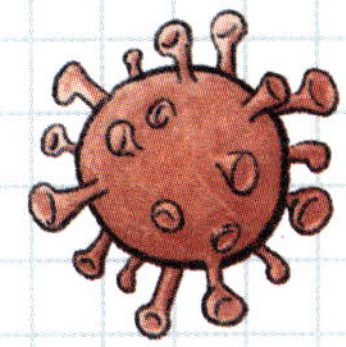

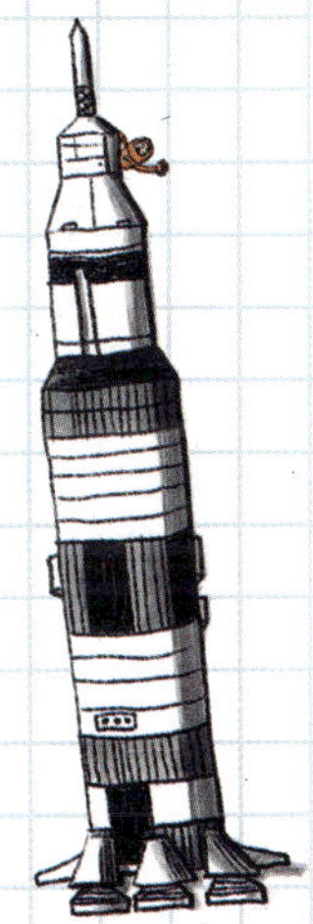

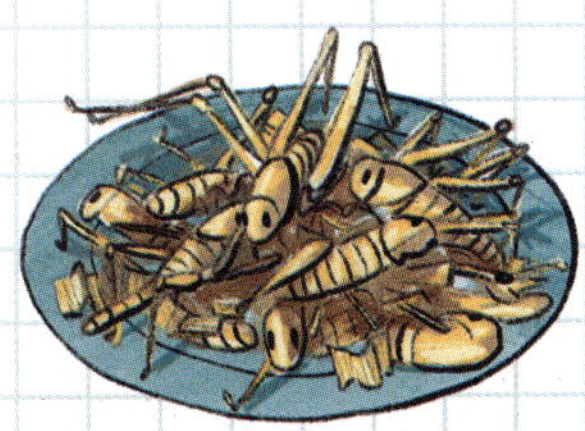

Explore, experiment, get messy!

This book is all about the weird and wonderful, messy and magical, extremely experimental world of science!

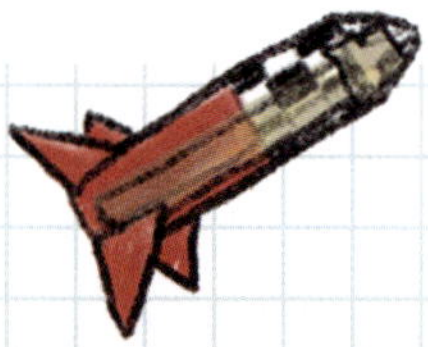

Science stuff to do!

In these pages, you'll find out how to ...

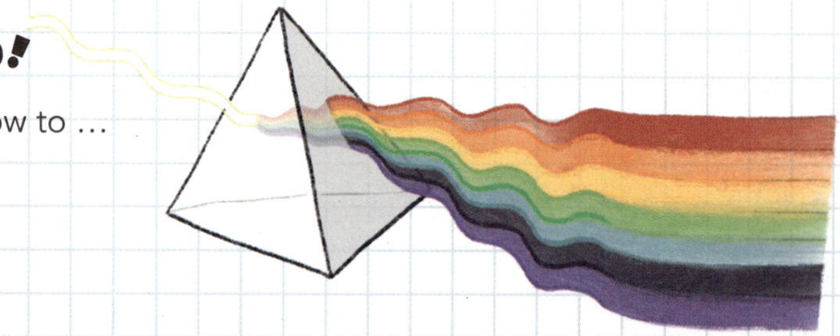

- Launch a rocket, go star-spotting, and dye your dinner.

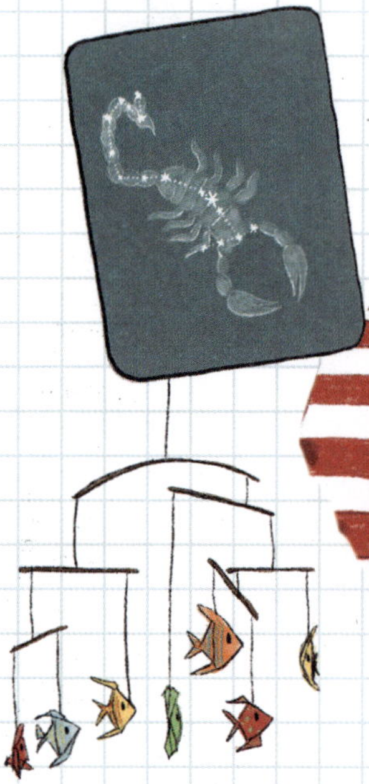

- Conjure up rainbows, make magnetic magic, and turn a room into a camera.

- Create your own mobile, molecule models, and a mini movie!

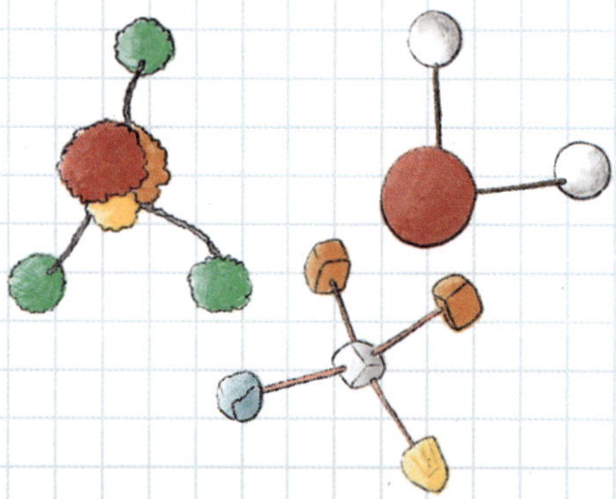

- Read tree rings, fit fossils together, and weave a spiderweb.

- Experiment with eyes, eggs, exercise, rocks, and reaction times.

- Be a weather scientist, an aircraft engineer, and an illusion artist!

- And make a hole in your hand.

Mess it up!

Most of all, this book is about trying things out, exploring, experimenting, and seeing what you can create, test, design, and discover. On every page, there's space to try out a science puzzle, artwork, lab test, activity, or game.

Let's go!

Turn the page, and let the experimenting begin ...

Rocket science!

People sometimes say, "It's not rocket science!" Well on this page, it definitely is!

Gas tube

A space rocket is basically a ginormous tube full of fuel.

The engine burns the fuel, making large amounts of gas. This pushes down out of the bottom of the rocket, then pushes it up!

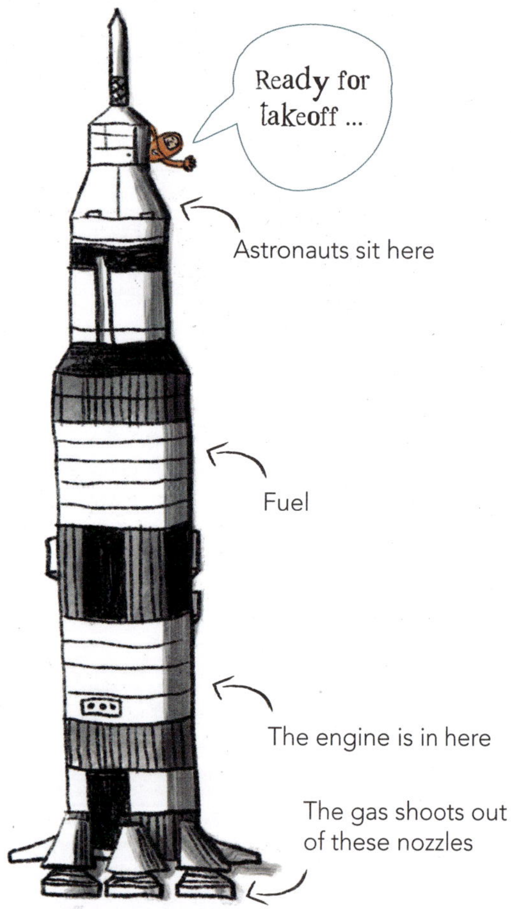

Make a mini rocket

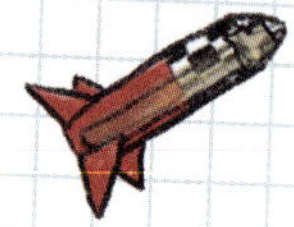

All you need is a flexible straw, paper, and glue or tape.

Cut a piece of paper about 5 x 8 cm (2 x 3 in) in size, and roll it around the straw.

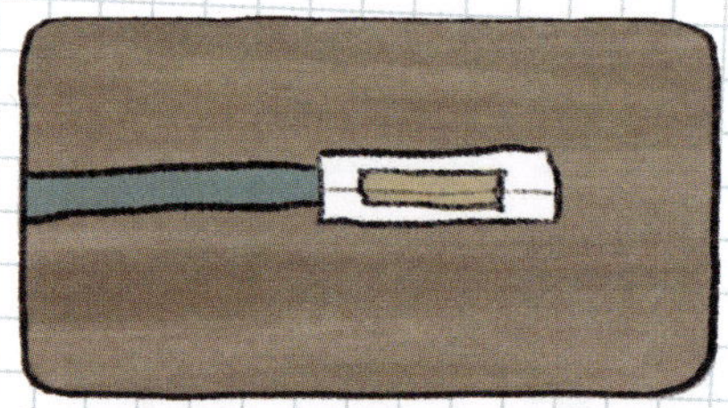

Glue or tape the paper to make a loose-fitting tube.

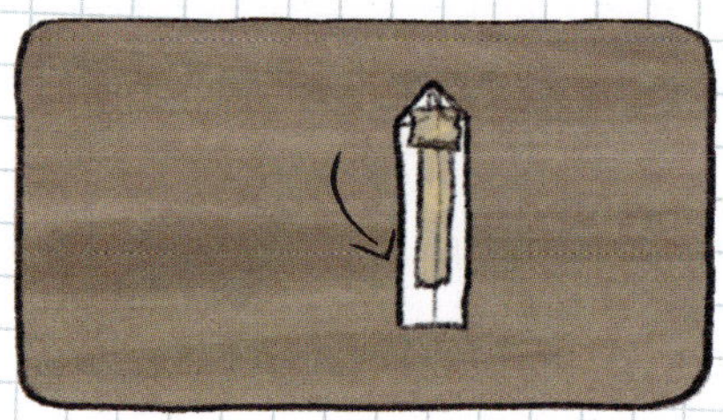

Remove the straw. Pinch the top of the paper tube into a point, and seal with glue or tape.

If you like, add paper fins or decorations.

3, 2, 1 ...

Fit your rocket over the short end of the straw ... | ... aim upward ... | ... blow into the straw, and ... WE HAVE LIFT OFF!

Now choose your space destination!

Let's make a game! Write a score for each space object in the circles.

Uranus

Venus

Mars

Jupiter

The International Space Station

Lean the book up against a wall, aim, and launch!

What's this? Find out on page 35!

Moon mysteries

It's round, it's white, it lights up the night ... but how does the Moon work?

Let's take a closer look!

In 1609, telescopes were a new invention. Top expert and all-round experimenter Galileo Galilei was keen to get his hands on one. So he built one himself and pointed it at the night sky.

Galileo was amazed. He saw that the Moon wasn't smooth, as it usually looked. It had mountains and bumpy parts, just like Earth.

He also discovered something amazing—other planets had moons, too!

Galileo's drawing of the Moon and its bumpy surface

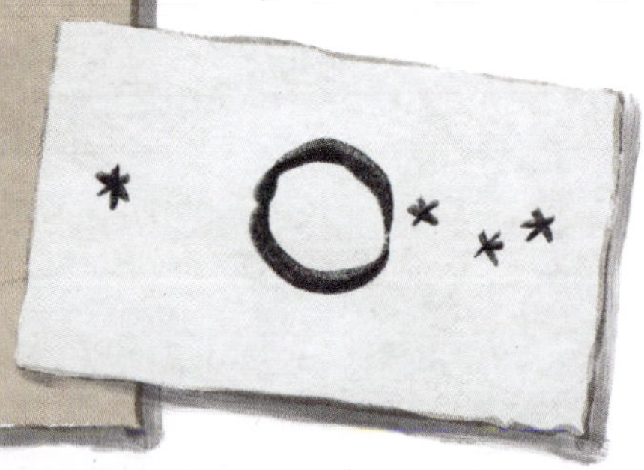

Galileo counted four moons moving around Jupiter.

Where is the Moon?

When we see the Moon in the sky, it looks quite close. It's actually about 384,400 km (238,855 mi) away.

Here's the Earth floating in space. If the Earth is this big, take a guess where the moon should be. Draw an X in the box where you think it goes, then check the answer on page 94.

Changing Shape

Each night, the Moon looks different. It seems to change, and goes through a series of shapes. They're called the phases of the Moon.

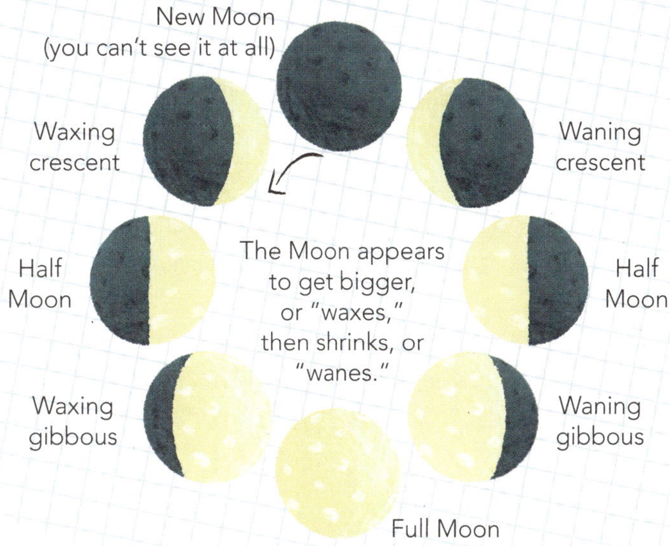

This happens because the Moon orbits around the Earth, roughly once every 28 days. As it moves around, it reflects light from the Sun. The shape we see depends on how much of the Moon is lit up. To see how it works, here's a simple experiment.

1 In a fairly dark room, switch on a small lamp—that's your Sun!

2 Hold up a small white ball, such as a polystyrene craft ball (stick it onto a pencil or cocktail stick if you have one). That's the Moon, and you are the Earth.

3 Now slowly turn around, holding the ball up so that it "orbits" around you.

Our place in Space

The Solar System is our own local area of space. It includes the Sun and all the planets around it.

Sun in the middle

The Sun is a star. It's the biggest object in the Solar System and has very strong gravity.

Whirling planets

The planets are eight big balls of rock, liquid, or gas that orbit (or circle) around the Sun. They're all different sizes.

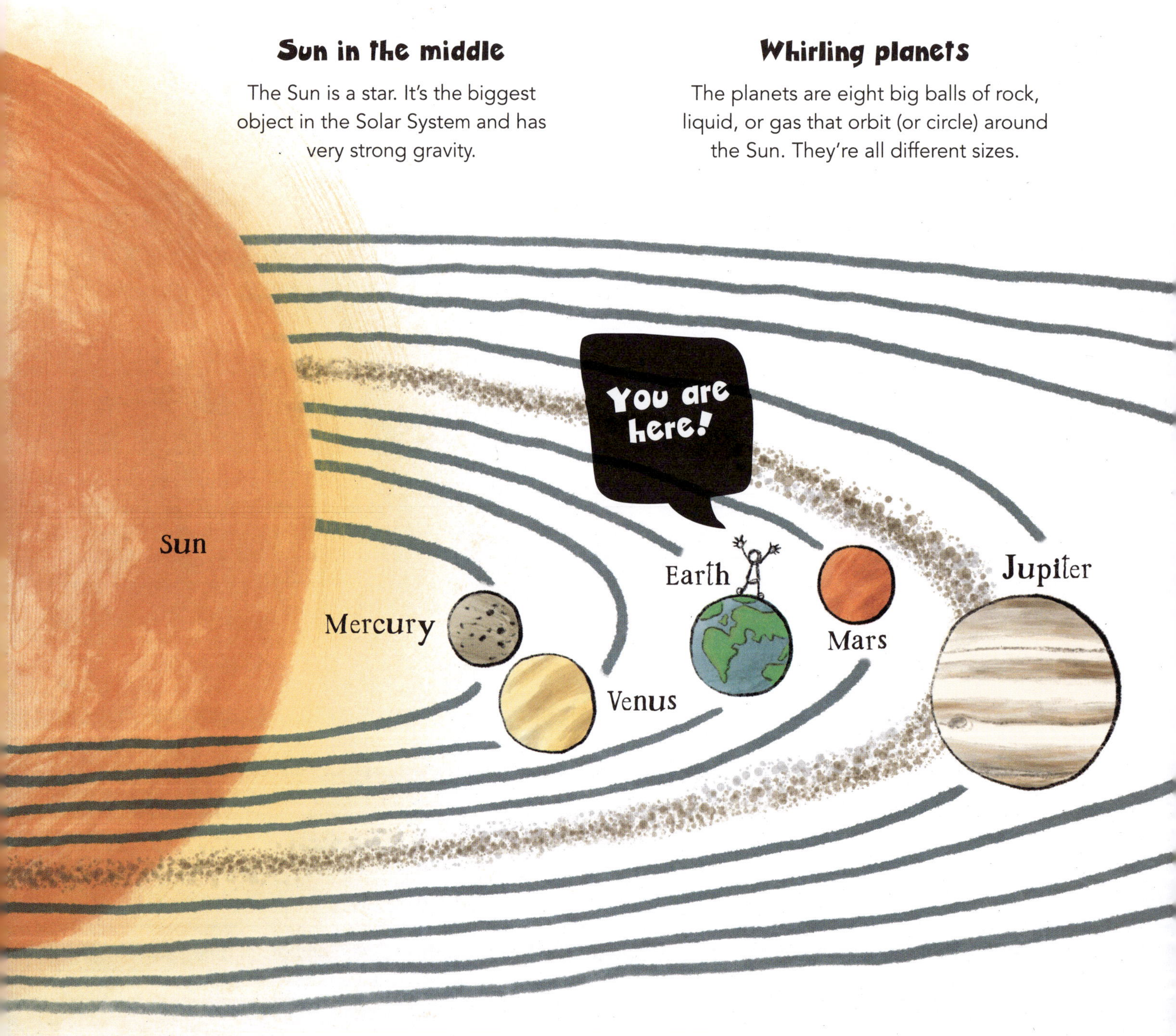

Remember the planets!

To remember the names of the planets in order of their distance from the Sun, write down their initial letters:

M_____	V_____	E_____	M_____	J_____	S_____	U_____	N_____
(for Mercury)	(for Venus)	(for Earth)	(for Mars)	(for Jupiter)	(for Saturn)	(for Uranus)	(for Neptune)

Then make them into a funny sentence to help you remember.
For example, it could be:

My Very Educated Monkey Just Served Up Noodles

Or:

Mr. Vulture Enjoys Mango Juice Sitting Under Newspapers

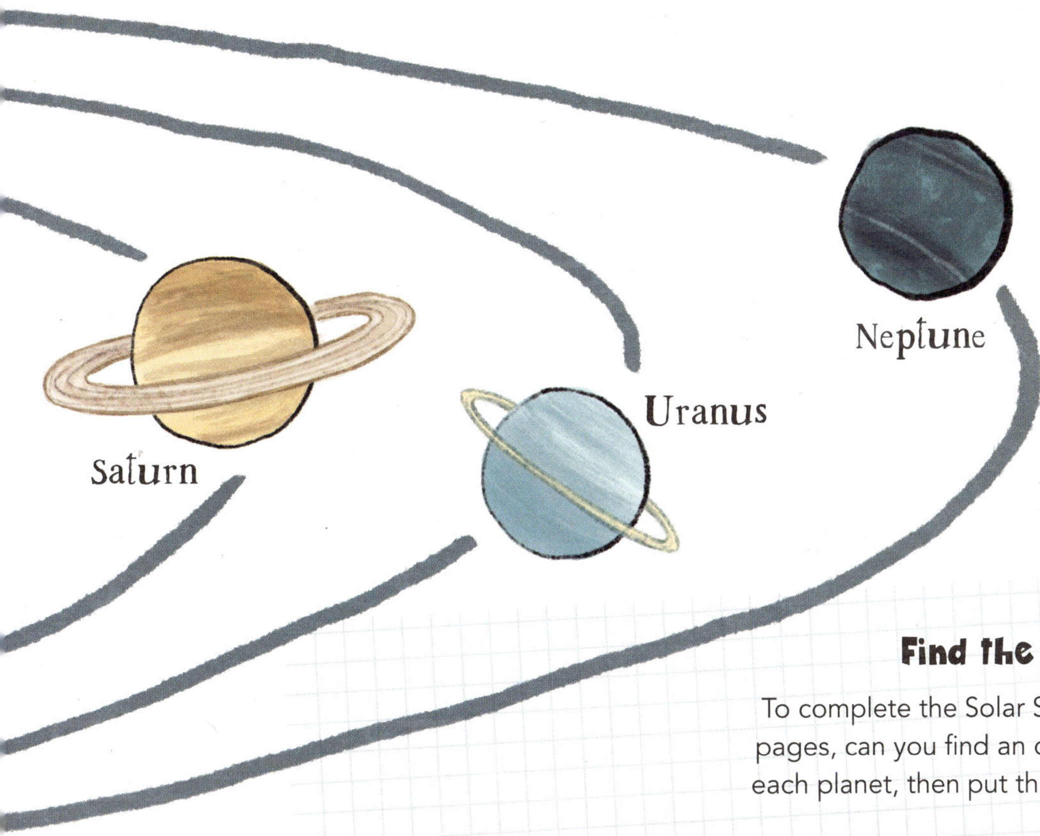

Find the planets!

To complete the Solar System diagram on these pages, can you find an object the relative size for each planet, then put them all in the right places?

See what fits best!

Time shadows

The Earth is constantly spinning around.
And as it spins, shadows move ...

How it works

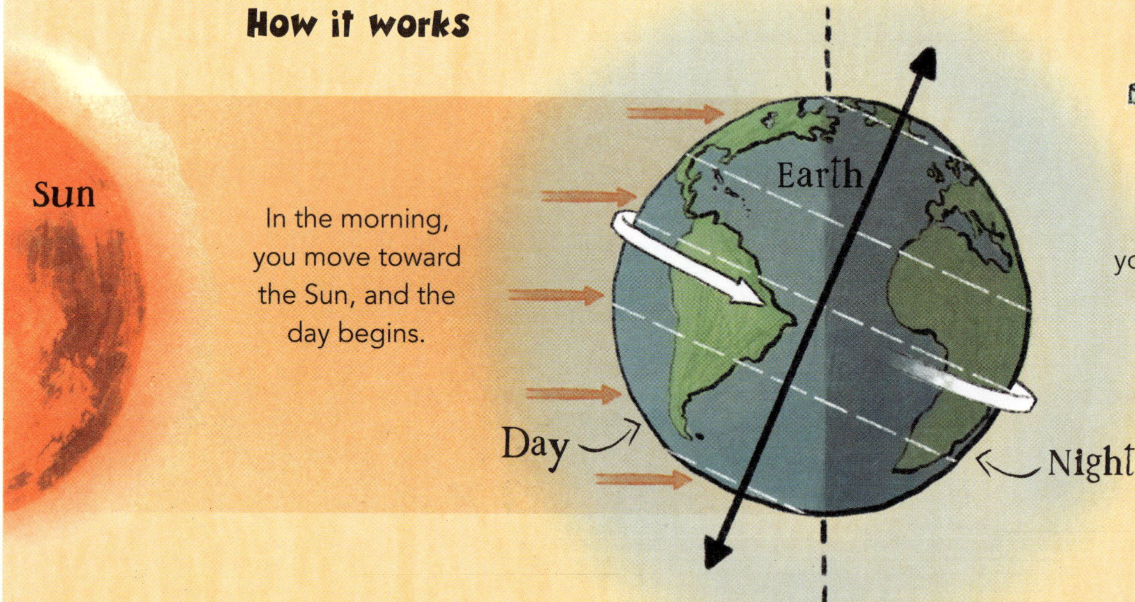

In the morning, you move toward the Sun, and the day begins.

Night falls as you move out of the sunlight.

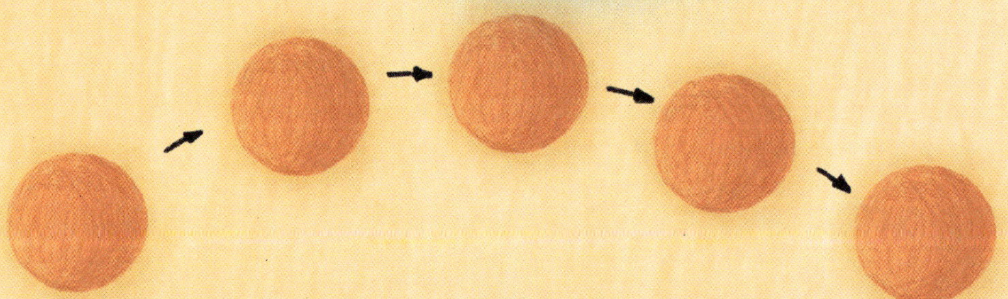

That's why, as the day goes by, the Sun seems to move across the sky ...

... and your shadow changes position.

Shadow clocks

For thousands of years, people have been using these changing shadows to tell time.

And they've made shadow clocks, too, such as sundials.

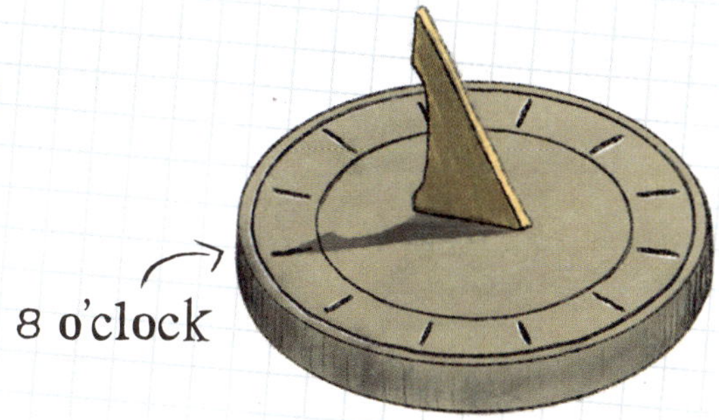

The lines on a sundial show different times. The shadow shows what time it is!

Draw the shadow

Watch a shadow move across this page!

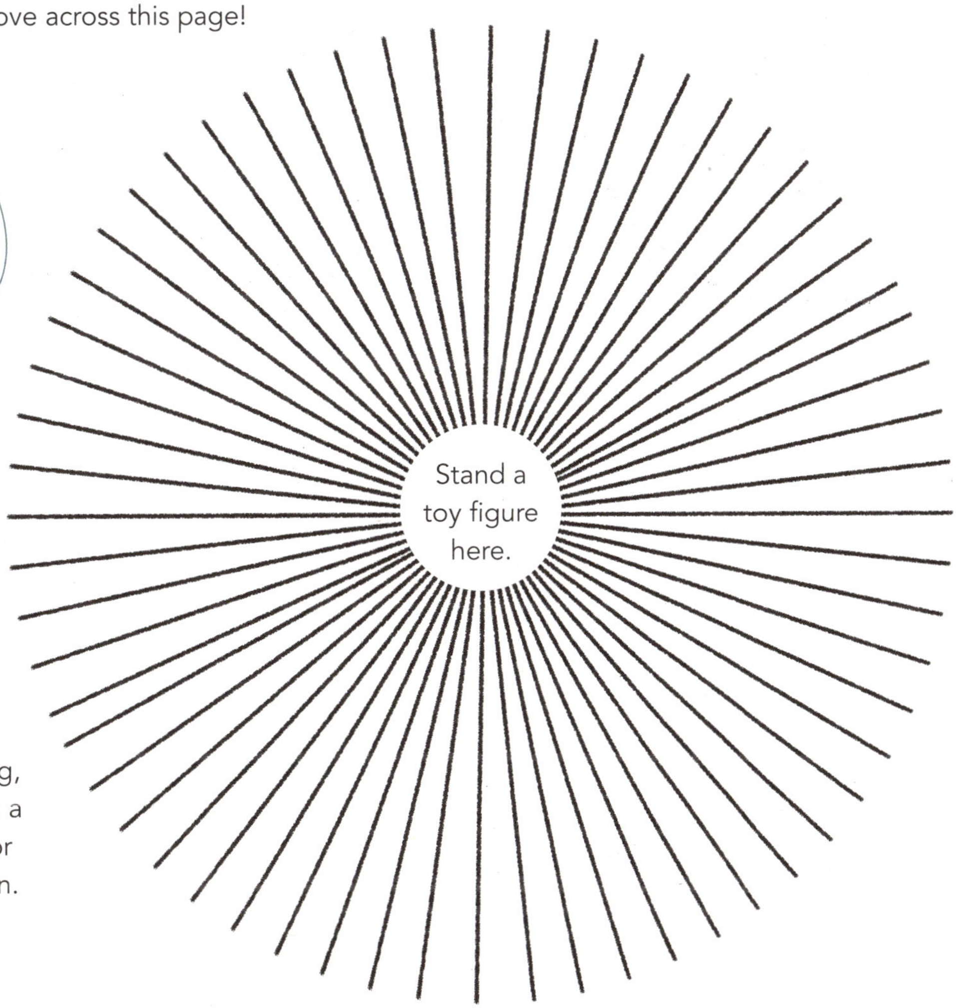

Early in the morning, lay the book flat on a sunny windowsill or anywhere in the sun.

Look at the toy figure's shadow, and carefully draw around it with a pencil.

Do the same again once every hour.

Can you mark the hours on the dial?

Star Science

The sky at night is full of twinkling lights—the stars!

What are stars?

Stars are giant balls of burning, exploding, glowing gases.
But they look small, because they're very far away!

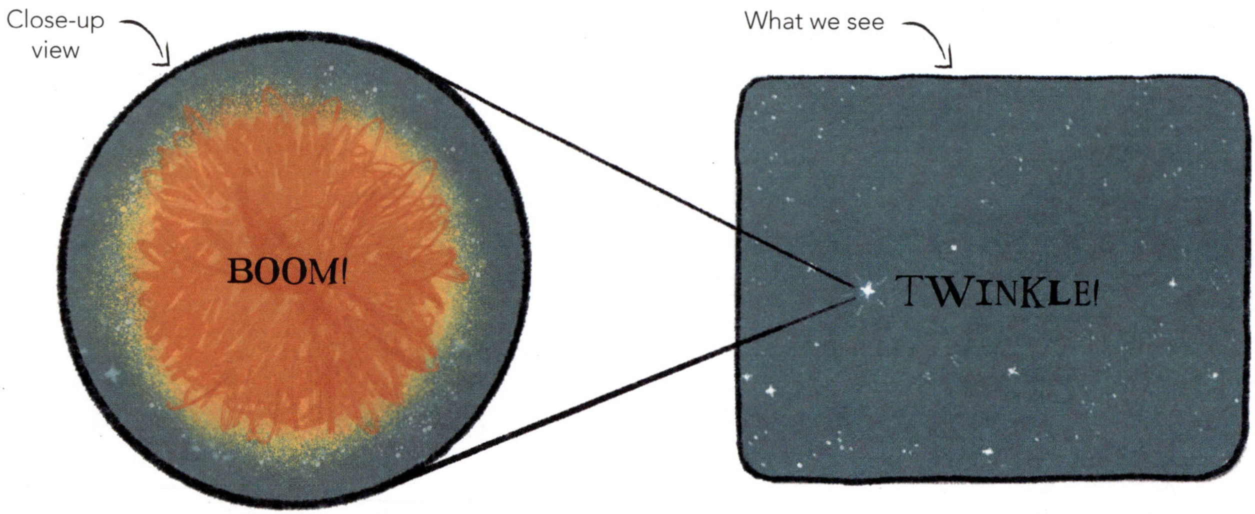

Long-distance light

When you see the stars, you're looking back in time!

HOW???

Light takes time to travel from the stars to your eyes.
For example, the star Vega is ...

239,356,480,956,294 km (148,729,221,941,545 mi) away!

Though light moves very fast, that's a LOOOONG way.
Light from Vega takes about 25 years to reach us.
So we see Vega as it looked 25 years ago!

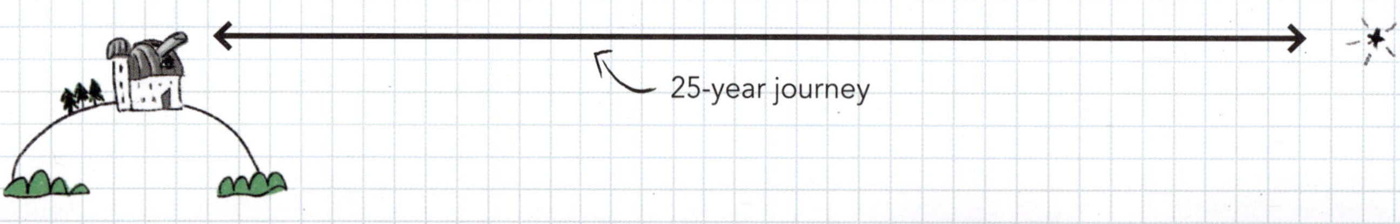

Seeing shapes

There are random patterns of stars all over the sky, but our brains can't help picking out familiar shapes. We call them constellations and throughout history we have given them different names. For example:

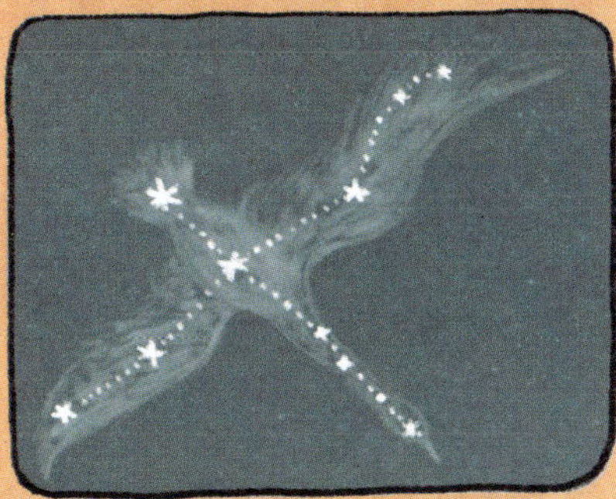

Cygnus, the swan

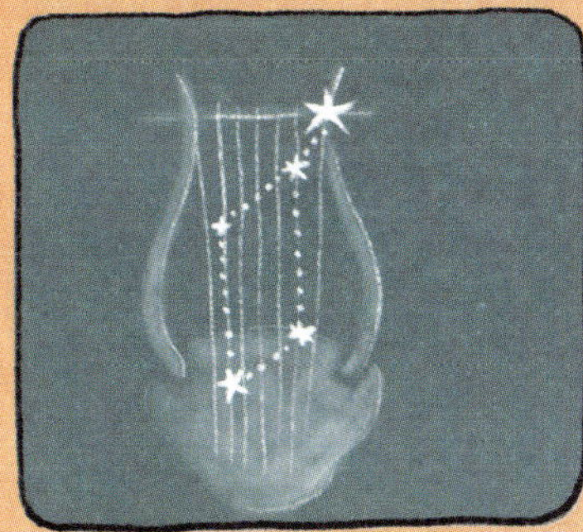

Lyra, the harp

Scorpius, the scorpion

Star-spotting

Can you find the three constellations shown above in this starry night sky? When you find them, connect them with lines, or draw a picture on them. If you get stuck, you can find the answers on page 94.

The strongest shape

Can one shape be stronger than another?
Find out here!

We need shapes!

When we make or build things, we need them to stay up and not fall apart.

So we need strong materials, but it also helps to use strong shapes.

Shape test

For this activity you will need a pile of books, tape, and three sheets of paper or card.

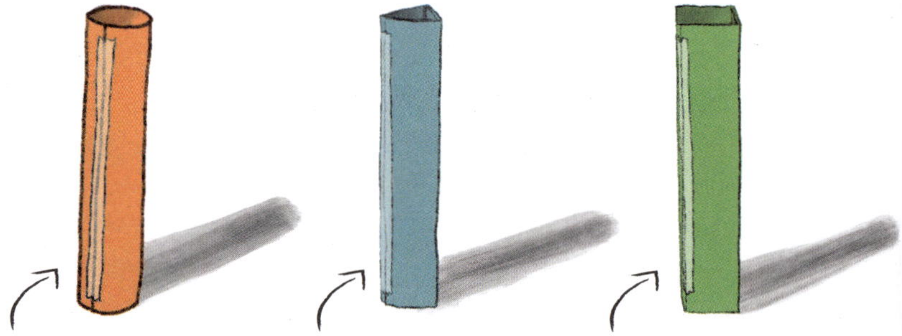

Roll one piece into a cylinder, and tape it in place.

Fold one into a triangle tube with three sides ...

... and fold one into a square tube with four sides.

First, decide which you think will be the strongest. Then test it!

Here's how!

Choose a tube and stand it upright on the floor. Balance a book on it. Keep adding more books until the shape crumples! Do the same with the other two tubes.

HOW MANY BOOKS COULD EACH TUBE SUPPORT?

Square tube: ____ books

Triangular tube: ____ books

Cylindrical tube: ____ books

Which one could hold the most books?

Which came in second?

Make a stool!

Now that you've got your results, could you make a stool out of cardboard strong enough to sit on?

Corrugated cardboard boxes and packaging are the best type to use.

Draw your design here.

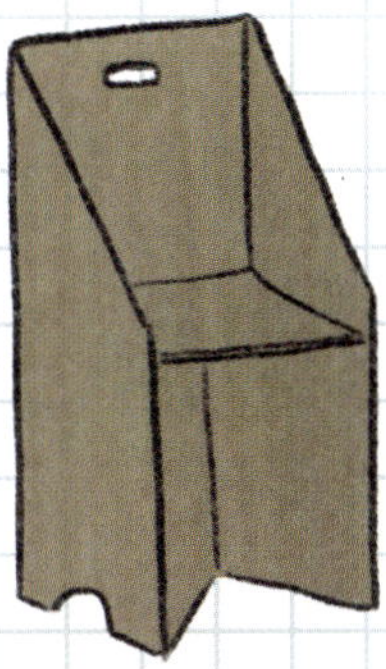

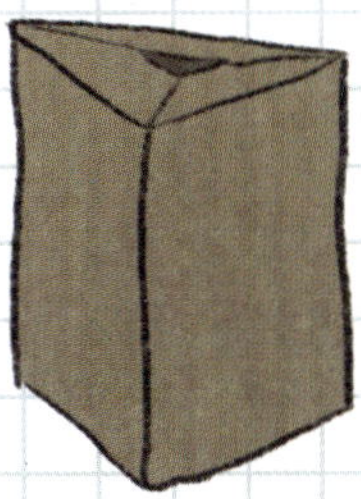

Magnetic magic

Magnets are amazing! They can pull things across empty space. But how?

How it works

Some metals are made of tiny parts that pull on each other.

Usually, they point in different directions.

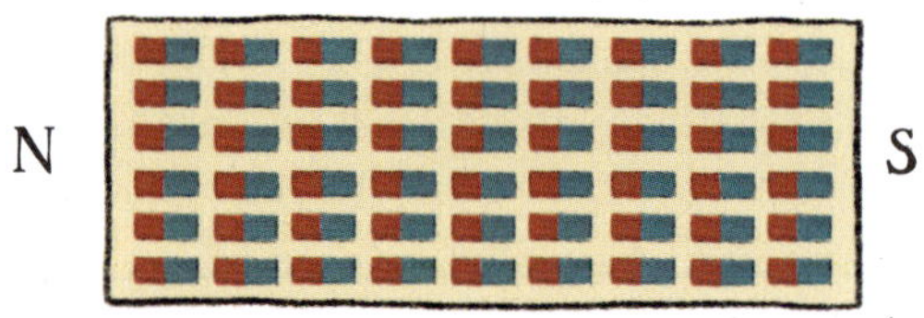

But in a magnet, they all point the same way.

A magnet can pull on metals like iron and steel.

Try these fun magnet experiments …

Hanging upside down!

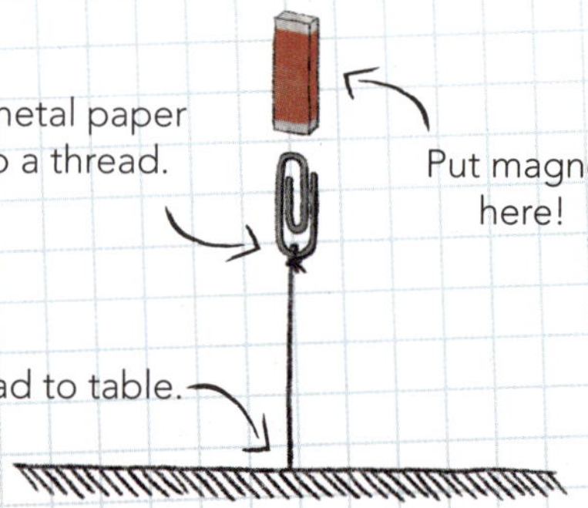

Magnet painting!

Move magnet around to move the paper clip and make it paint a picture.

Magnet fishing

Make a magnet fishing rod with a stick and some string. Move the magnet around using your fishing rod.

Pulling forces

Gravity is a bit like magnetism, when you think about it.

It also pulls objects toward each other even when they're not touching.

Magnet maze

Here's a maze waiting to be solved!

Hold a magnet underneath the page.

Put a steel paper clip on top.

Flying machines

What's the best way to make a piece of paper fly? Try it, and see!

Paper darts

Here's a set of instructions for a simple paper dart. Start with a piece of letter paper, and get folding ...

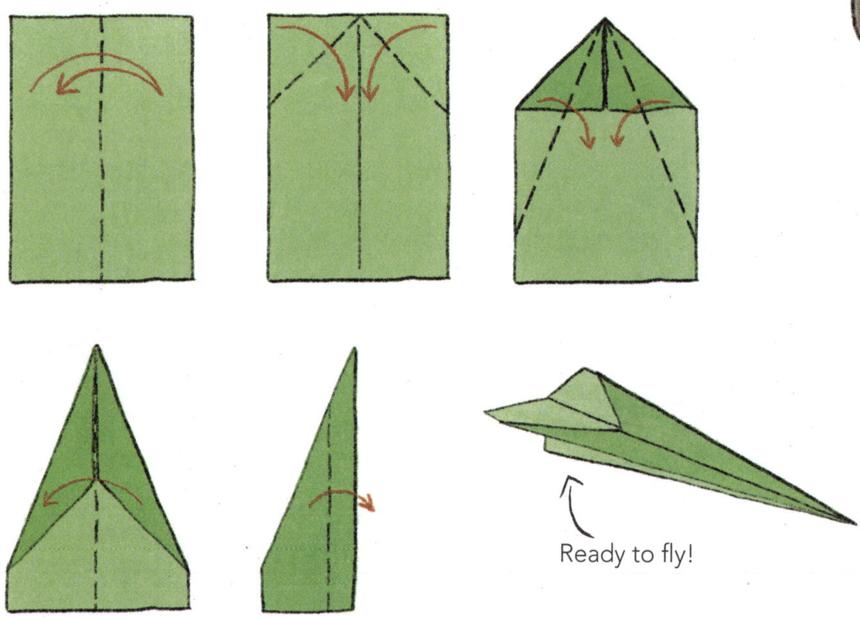

To launch your dart, hold it up high, and push it forward and slightly upward.

How it works

Planes fly by zooming forward, pushing air down as they go.

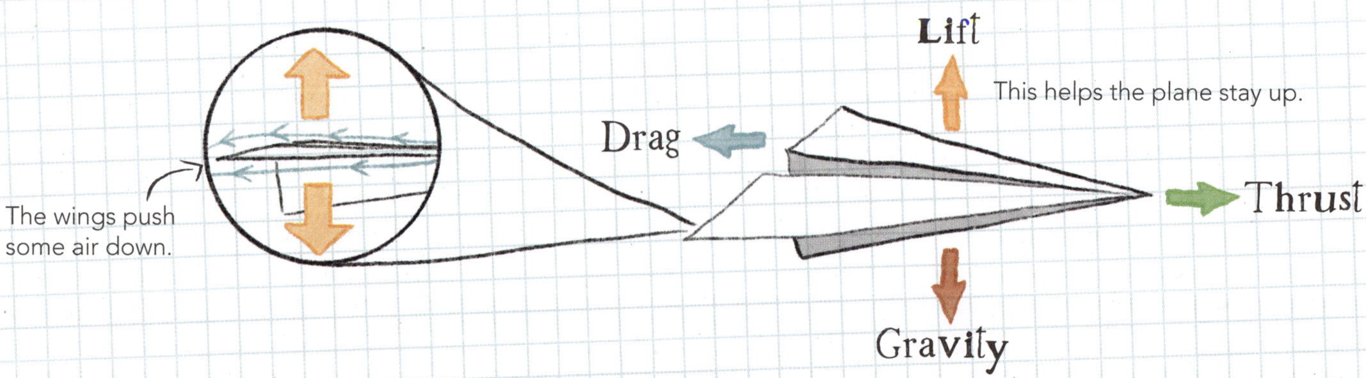

As the plane slows, it falls down.

Can you invent your own designs, too?
Here are some more ideas!

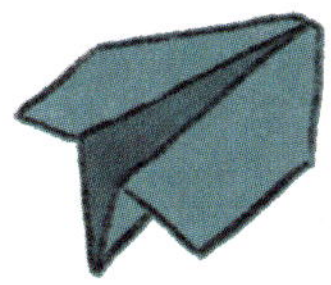

Mess around!

Once you've tried a classic dart, start experimenting ...

Flaps and folds

Flaps or extra folds on the wings control the flow of air. Try it!

Add weight

A little weight can help balance the plane and make it fly farther.

Try adding tape, paper clips, small coins, or card.

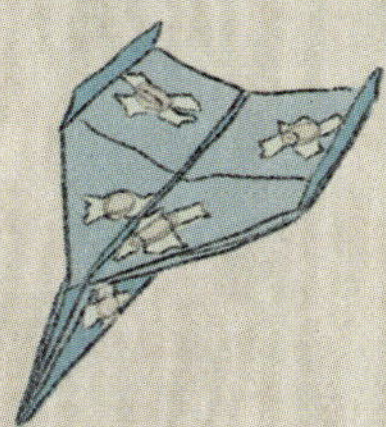

The fabulous flying tube

Did you know a tube can fly? Try this!

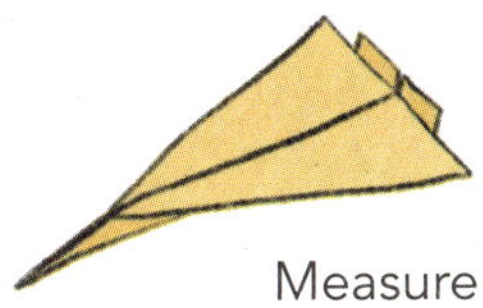

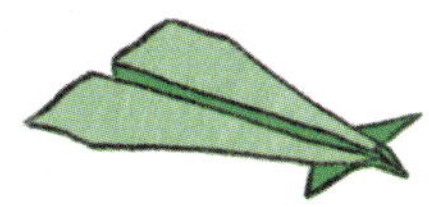

Flying race

Measure the distances your planes can fly.

Draw and name each plane you make here, and fill in its top distance record!

Name: ________________ **Distance record:** __________

Name: ________________ **Distance record:** __________

Name: ________________ **Distance record:** __________

Name: ________________ **Distance record:** __________

Name: ________________ **Distance record:** __________

Make it balance!

How do things balance? Find out in these experiments.

Make a mobile

You'll need thread or string, wooden skewers or sticks, and small objects.

Ask an adult to hang up a piece of string somewhere safe, like in a doorway.

Tie it to a stick, and tie more string to each end.

Then try tying on different objects so that they balance.

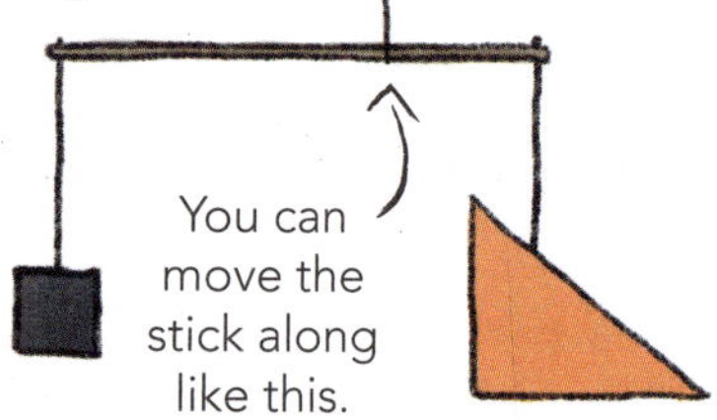

Balancing bird

This bird will balance on your fingertip, thanks to weights that make its wing tips extra-heavy.

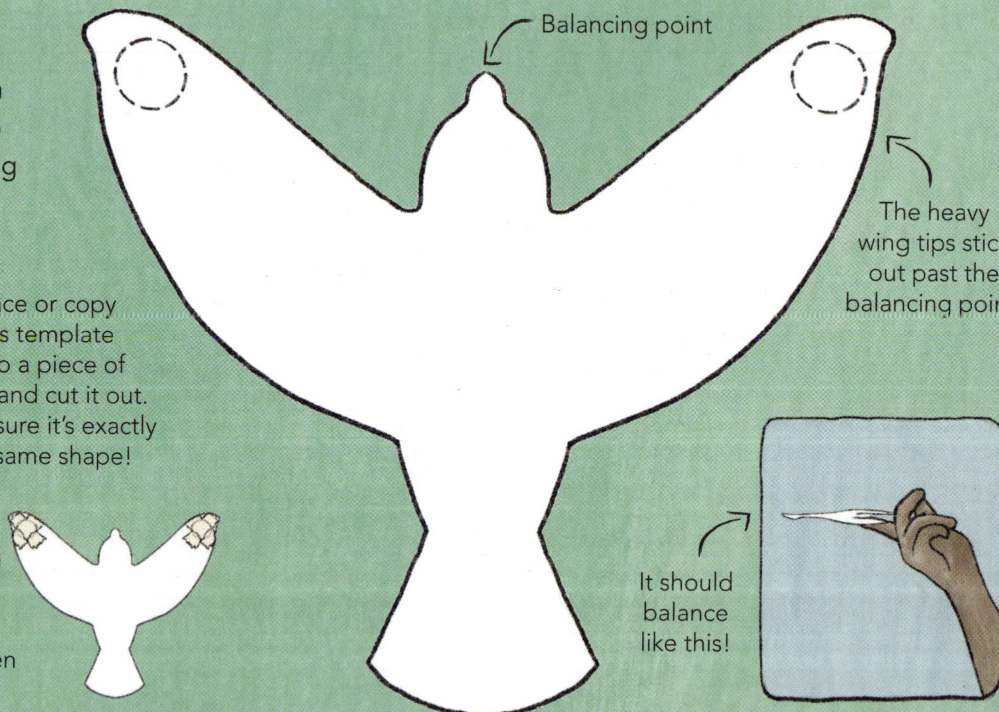

Trace or copy this template onto a piece of card, and cut it out. Make sure it's exactly the same shape!

Tape two small coins where the circles are, then turn your bird over.

It should balance like this!

Design your own balancing beast

Now design your own balancing shape, taking inspiration from the bird. It needs a balancing point and parts that stick out past the balancing point, where you can put the coins.

Here are some ideas!

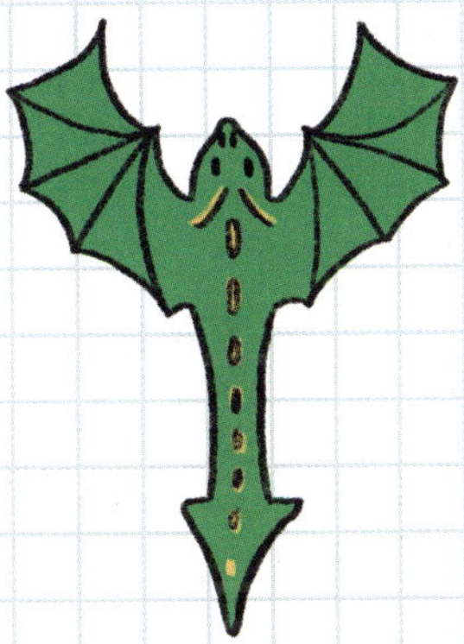

Heat rises

You may have heard that "heat rises"—but why?

This could be messy!

Do this experiment in the kitchen or bathroom in case of spills, with an adult to help.

Put a few drops of food dye in the bottle, and carefully fill it with cold water.

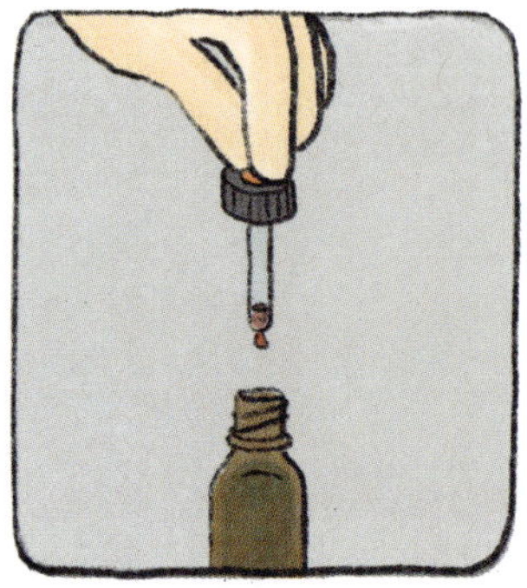

With your finger on the top, stand the bottle in the container—then remove your finger!

What happens?

Now repeat the experiment, but fill the small bottle with HOT tap or faucet water and food dye.

Moving up!

The cold water stays still, but the hot water flows upward.

When water heats up, it get bigger and lighter. So cooler water sinks, and warmer water rises up.

Snake spiral!

It works with air, too!

Trace or copy this snake onto paper.

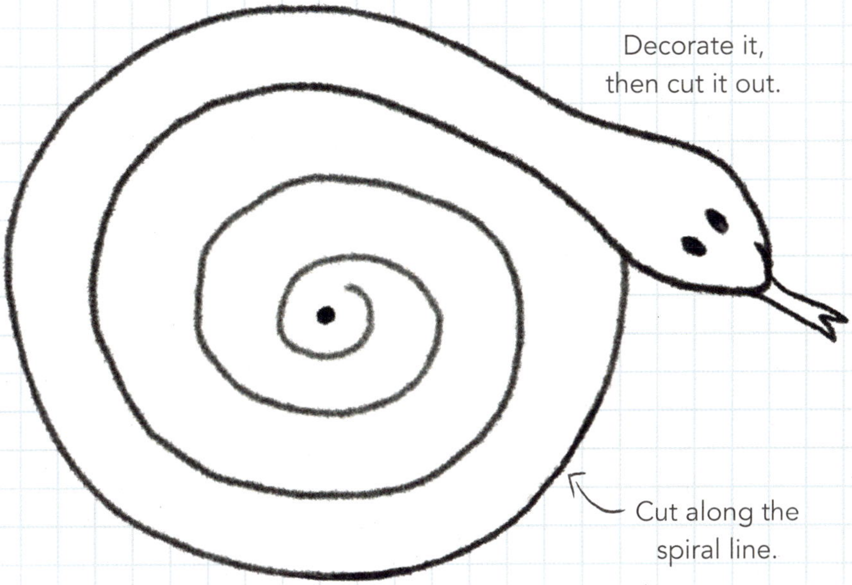

Decorate it, then cut it out.

Cut along the spiral line.

Tape a thread to the tail, and hang or hold it up above a heater.

Can you make a square version?

Freaky Friction

You're climbing a rocky slope in a pair of rubber-soled sneakers. Why don't you slip off? Friction!

Scraping, slowing, and stopping

Friction happens when two surfaces rub or scrape together.

Friction between sneakers and rocks make them grip.

Brakes on a bike use friction to slow down and stop the wheel.

Friction makes it hard to push a heavy box along the floor.

Friction and materials

Which materials have the most friction?

Lean a tray or a piece of thick card on a few books to make a slope.

Put different objects near the top. Which slide down the fastest? Which get stuck?

An eraser is grippy and gets stuck—just like rubbery sneakers!

Coins slide down.

Slide and stop

Lay this book flat, and put a coin at the start line.

What else can you try?

Foam 

Cork 

Pebble 

Seashell 

Pencil 

Toys 

String 

Socks 

Can you flick the coin just hard enough to make it stop on the target?

START

At first, the coin moves fast, but friction with the paper slows it down.

Friction power!

Friction can do amazing things!

Friction glue

Did you know that friction can hold two books together, as if they were stuck with glue? You can test it out using this book and another similar book or magazine.

Turn one book over, so the edges of the pages face each other.

Overlap the pages of both books one at a time, like this:

First one from this book ...

... then from this book ...

... and keep going until you've used all the pages.

Press the books flat.

Then try to pull them apart. Bet you can't!

When just two pages touch each other, there's not that much friction.

But with all the pages together, it's super-powerful!

A world without friction

We use friction all the time. If it didn't exist, all surfaces would just slither and slide against each other! It would be very hard to pick things up, walk, or even eat!

It's hot!

Friction also makes things heat up. For example, if you slide down a rope too quickly, the friction will burn your hands.

Hold two identical coins on the two black dots on the middle of this page.

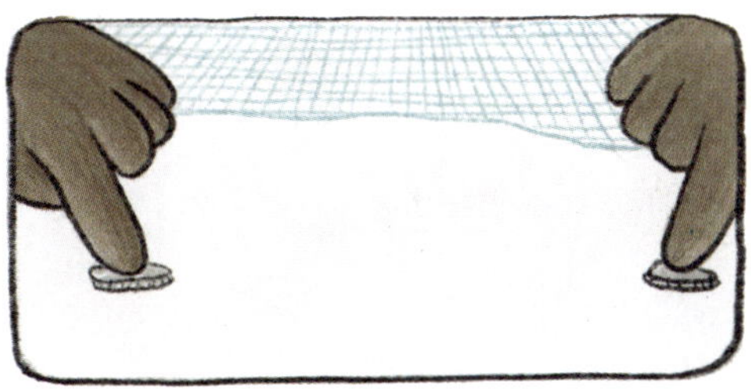

Keep one still. Rub the other to and fro quickly for 30 seconds.

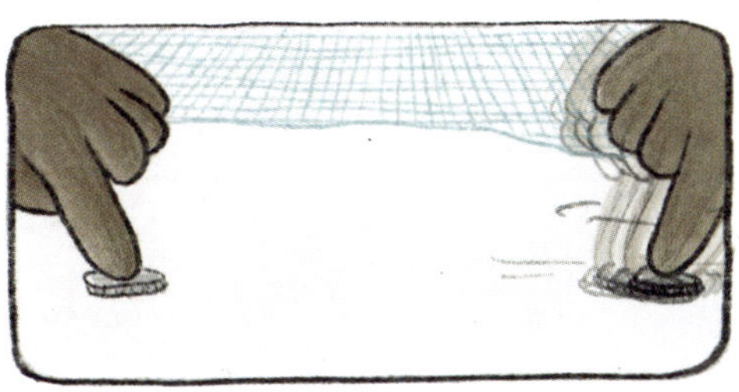

Seeing the light

We see things because our eyes can detect light.

Into your eyes

For example, light shines from the Sun ...

... hits a tree ...

... and reflects off it.

If reflected light enters your eyes, you see the tree!

Why are trees green?

Good question!

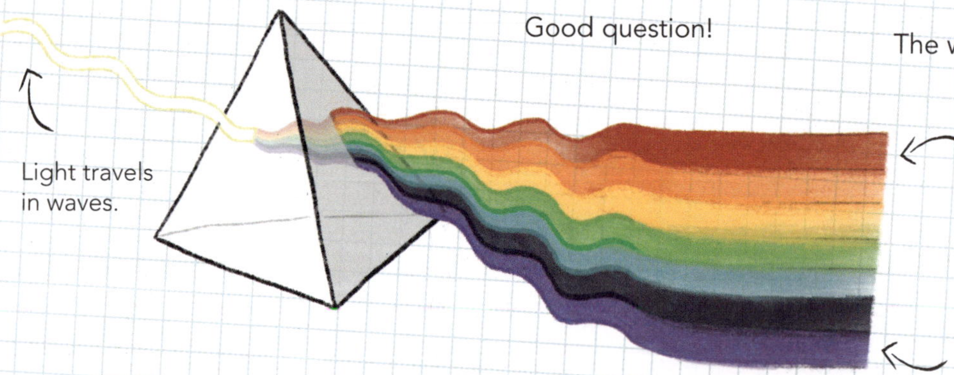

Light travels in waves.

The waves have different lengths.

The longest wavelengths look red.

The wavelengths in between are a rainbow, or spectrum, of different shades.

The shortest wavelengths look purple.

Leaves reflect the green wavelength the best, so they look green!

Make a rainbow!

You need a sunny day, white paper, and a glass of water.

Stand the water on the paper, so that the sun shines on the surface.

You should see a rainbow on the paper!

The water makes the light bend, or refract.

This splits it into different wavelengths.

Flip it!

Don't throw that water away!

Stand this book up, and put the glass of water about 15cm (6 in) in front of the lower arrow.

Look through the water, and you should see the arrow pointing the other way!

This happens because of the way the water bends the light.

The dark room

Catch a picture of the world inside a room!

How it works

If light from an object enters a small hole, the light rays swap around and make an upside-down image.

This happens inside our eyes:

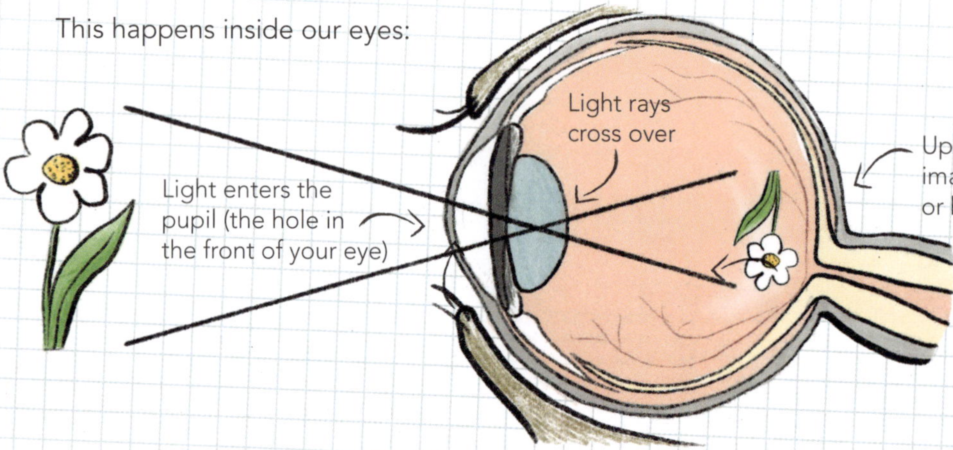

Dark room

You can also do this with a room. It's called a "camera obscura" meaning "dark room."

You need a room with a small window and a view of something, plus some cardboard from old boxes or a few large black refuse bags.

Ask an adult to help you tape the cardboard or bags over the windows so no light can get in (use removable tape).

Make a small round hole in the cardboard or plastic with pointed scissors.

What did you see?

After doing the experiment below, draw the image you saw in this space.

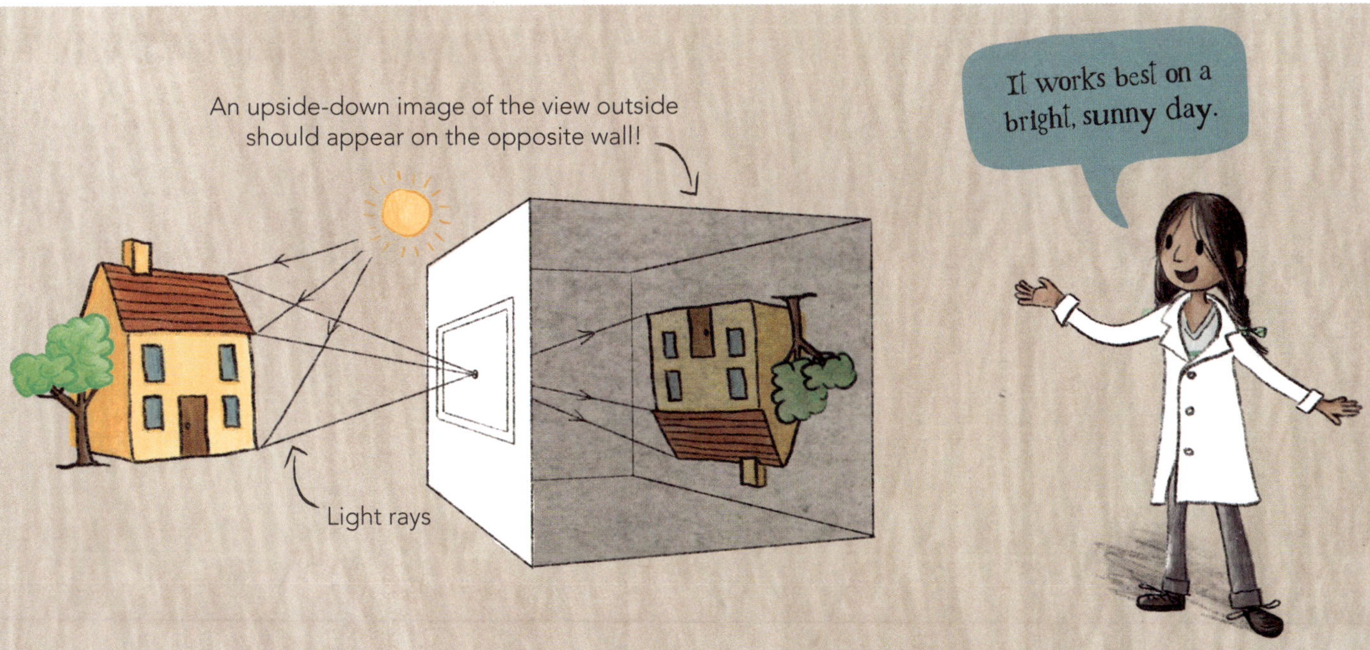

Flip pics

Make mini movies using nothing but a notebook and pen ...

All about animation

It's used in lots of TV shows and movies.

Animation works by showing us a series of pictures, each one slightly different from the one before.

If we see them fast enough, our brain blends them together, and it looks like movement.

Try it yourself!

Modern screen animations are made using computers, but long ago they were drawn on paper. You can do this, too, using a thick paperback notebook or a pad of sticky notes.

Start drawing a simple picture in the corner of the last page.

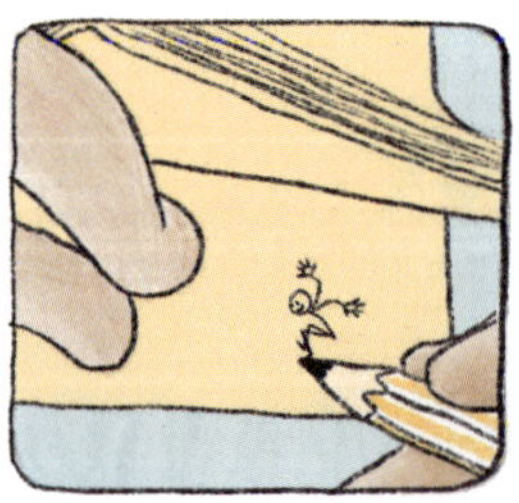

Do the same on the next page in the exact same place—but change the picture slightly to make it move and tell a story.

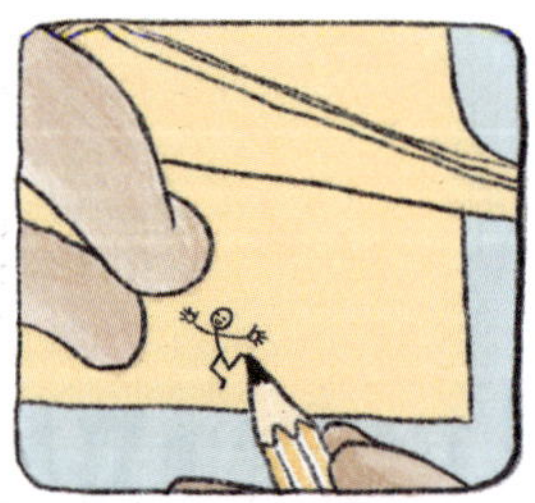

Keep going until you've drawn on all the pages.

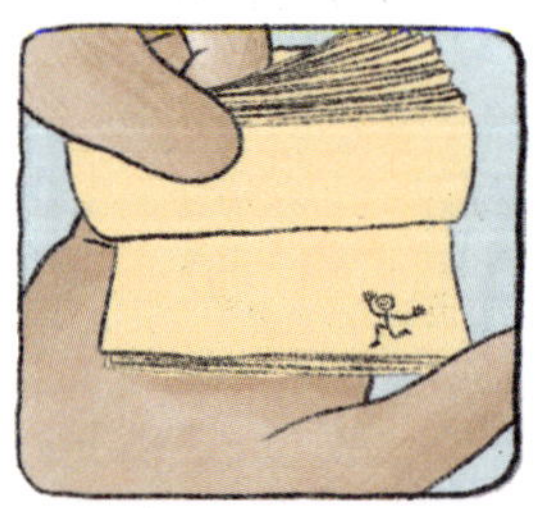

Then flip though from back to front to see your mini movie!

More ideas

If you're stumped about what to draw, here are some ideas ...

Storyboard space

You can use this space to test out ideas.

You can even use this book! There's a space on the corner of every page for making your own micro-movie!

Sound waves

When a dog barks or someone plays a drum, other people hear it. But how?

Vibrations in the air

Sound happens when objects shake to and fro, or vibrate. This can happen so fast that you can't see it.

Parts in the dog's throat vibrate when it barks.

Drum skin vibrates when drumstick hits it.

This makes the air around the object vibrate.

The vibrations spread through the air in waves, or sound waves.

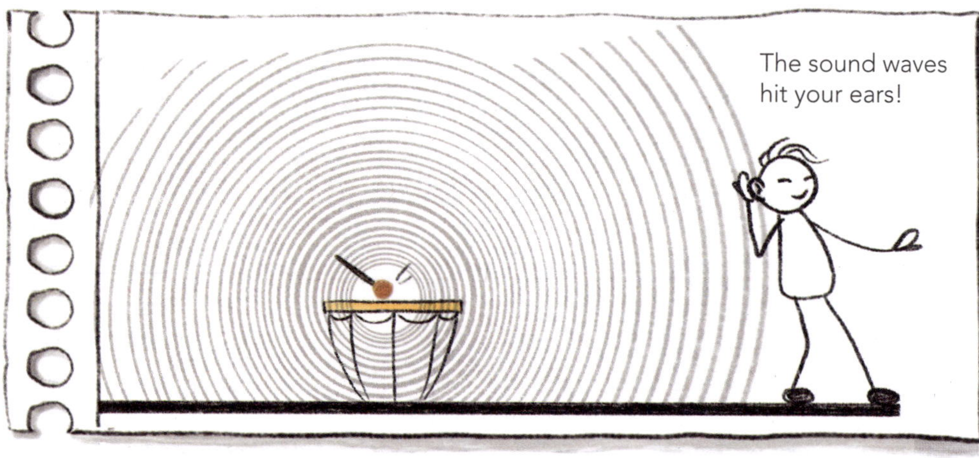

Feel the vibes!

You can feel sound waves using a balloon or bottle.

Play loud music on a radio or hi-fi.

Put your hands on a blown-up balloon or an empty plastic bottle, and hold it near the speaker.

You'll feel the vibrations!

Seeing sounds

Scientists sometimes show sound waves on a waveform graph, like this:

Different sounds have different waveforms—like these!

Someone coughing

Human heartbeat

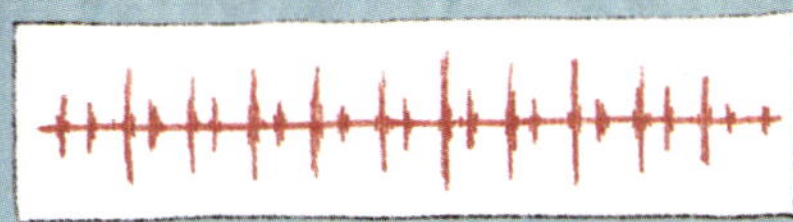

Toilet flushing

Dog barking

Two beats on a snare drum

Draw a sound

What do you think the waveform for a ticking clock would look like?

Mess with music!

Explore sound by making your own orchestra, and writing your own music!

What is music?

Music is made of patterns of different sounds, often with different notes, or pitches.

Pitch means how high or low a sound is.

Move to the beat

Music also has rhythms, or repeated beats and time patterns.

Crash! BOOM! Bang, bang, TINK!

Make musical instruments

Here are some easy musical instruments to make ... or invent your own!

Box guitar

Stretch rubber bands over an empty box, and pluck them.

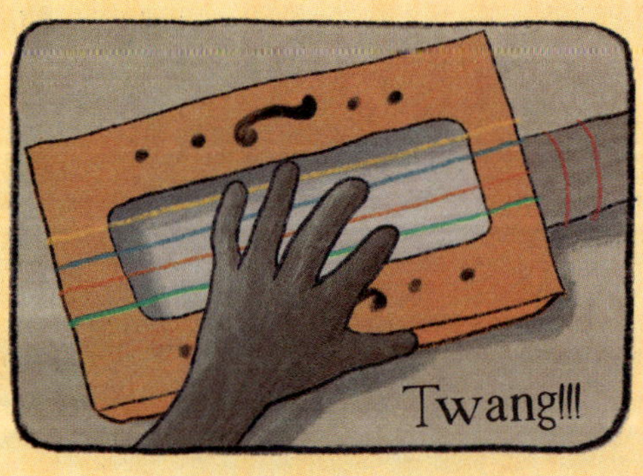

Straw trumpet

Flatten the tip of a straw, then cut it into a point.

Hold the straw between your teeth with the pointed end inside your mouth, and blow.

Shakers

Put beads, buttons, or dried lentils inside empty tubs or bottles.

Give them a shake!

Bottle organ

Fill glass bottles or jars with different amounts of water.

To play them, blow over the tops of the bottles.

Or tap with a spoon.

Tub drum

Turn over an old food container, and hit it with a wooden spoon.

Music notation

Musicians write music down on staves, like this:

Make up a way to write music for your instruments. For example:

You might use this for a shaker: 

Or this for a straw trumpet: 

Amazing atoms

All the materials and objects around us are made of tiny, invisible atoms!

What are they?

Atoms are a little bit like tiny balls. They come in lots of different types and sizes—but even the biggest ones are very, VERY small.

For example …

Hydrogen atoms are found in the Sun and in water.

The air contains **oxygen atoms**.

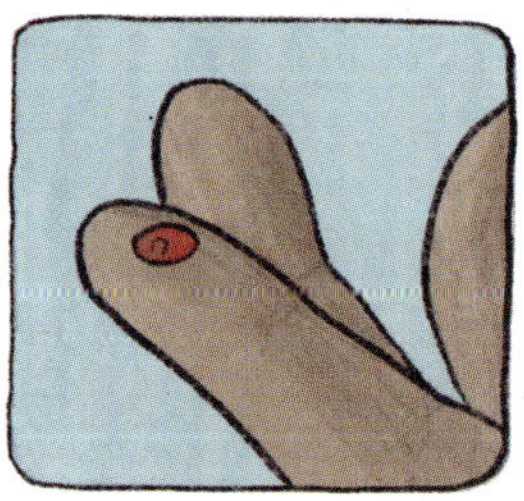

Iron atoms make iron. They're also in our blood!

Silver is made of **silver atoms**.

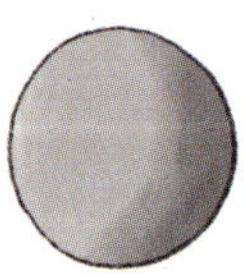

A closer look

Atoms are not like hard, solid balls. Instead, they are full of energy and movement.

Each atom has a middle part called a nucleus.

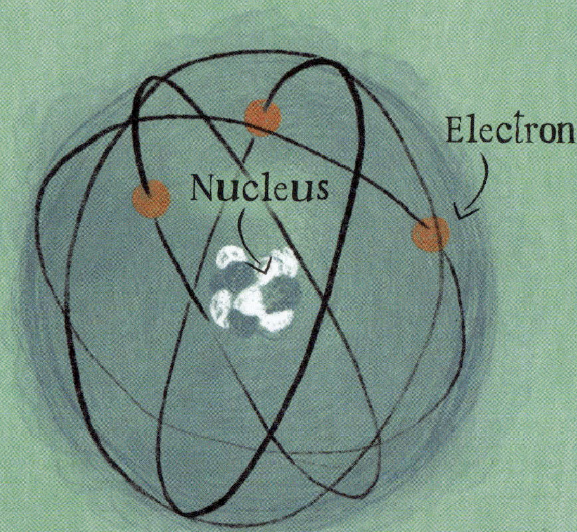

Tiny parts called electrons zoom around the nucleus.

Drawing atoms

Scientists draw atoms as diagrams like this:

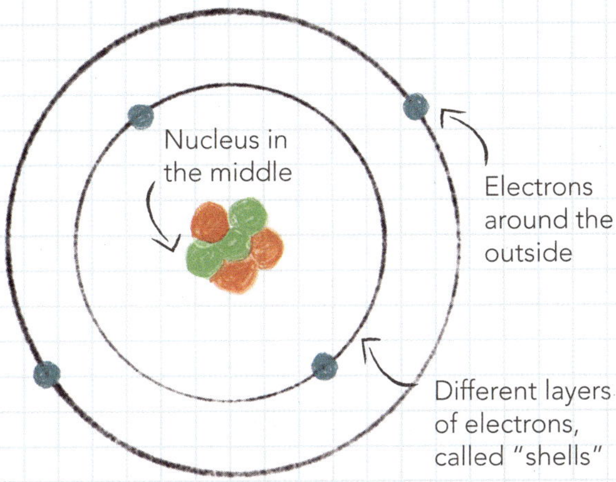

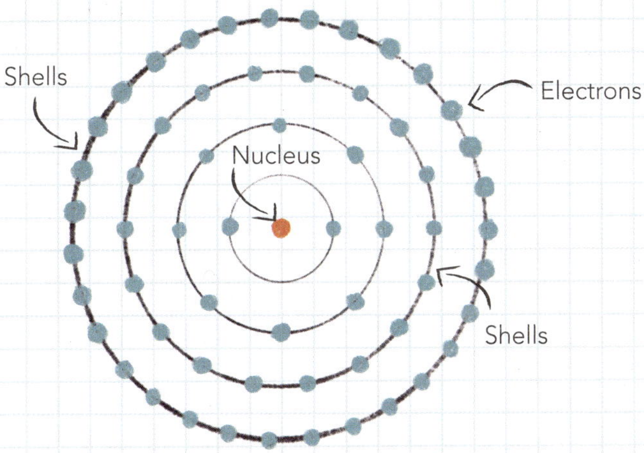

The first shell holds up to 2 electrons.

The second shell holds up to 8.

The third shell holds up to 18.

The fourth shell holds up to 32.

Heading

Can you fill in the electrons on these atoms?

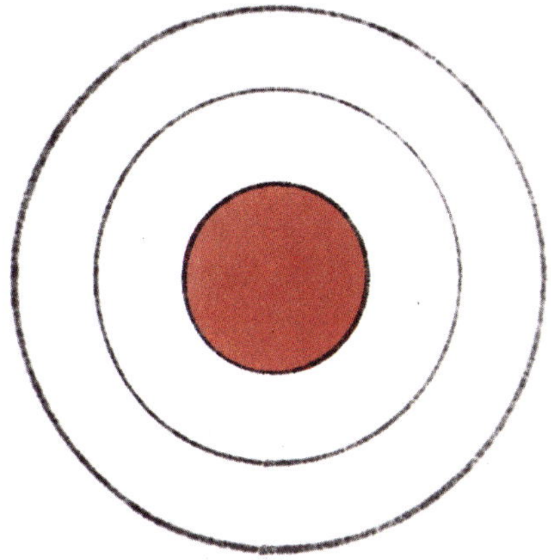

Oxygen has 8 electrons.

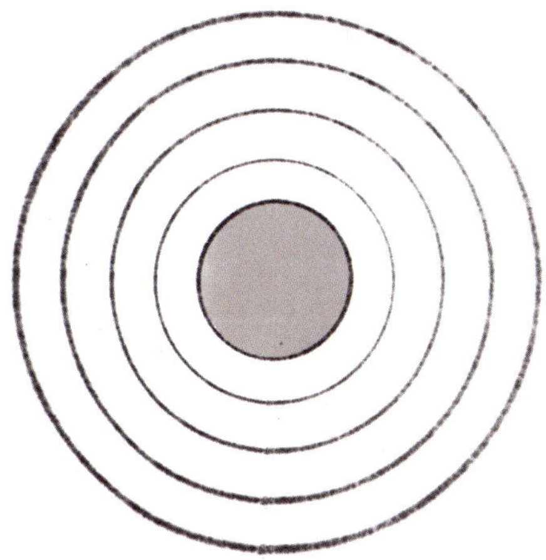

Iron has 26 electrons.

Making molecules

Some atoms exist on their own—but others join together to make molecules.

Like what?

Water is a common type of molecule.

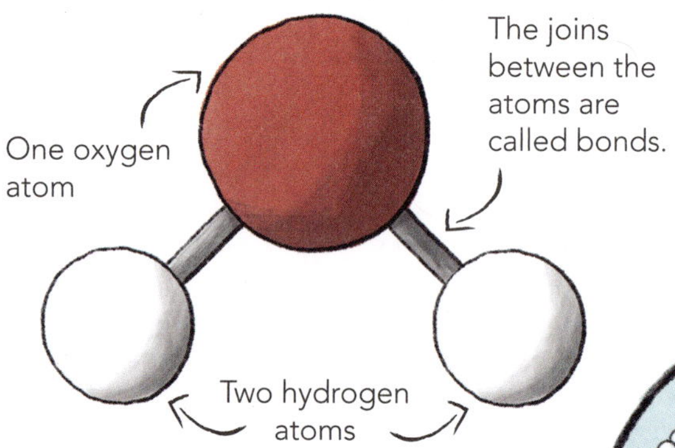

Each water molecule is made of 3 atoms joined together.

All the water we drink, plus the water in rain, rivers, and the sea, is made of water molecules like this.

Many molecules

There are many different types of molecules made of different atoms joined together in different patterns.

Salt molecule

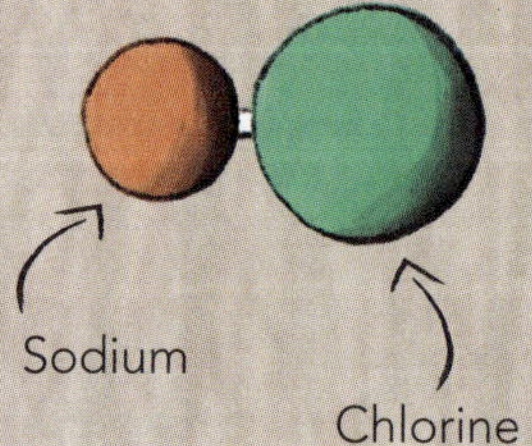

Carbon dioxide molecule

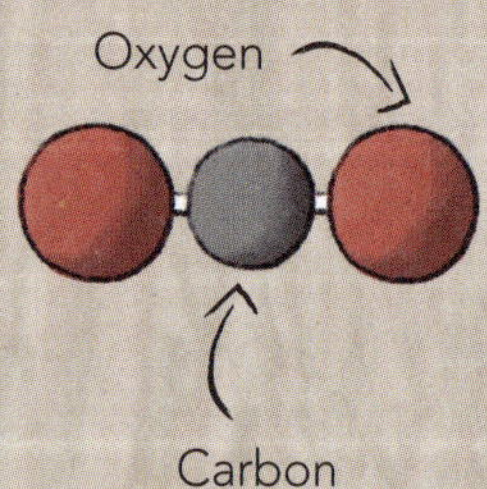

Diamond molecule

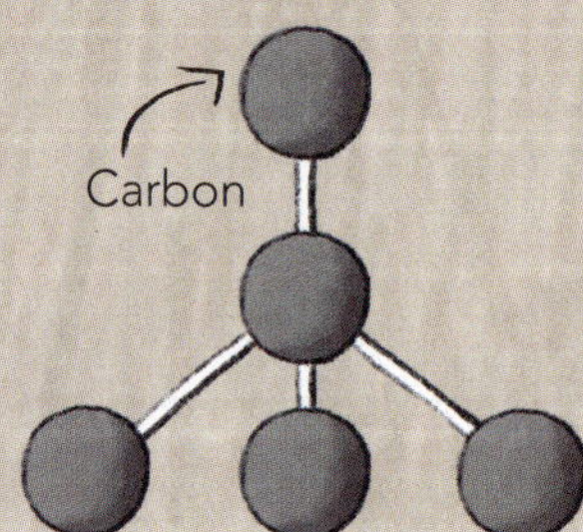

Baking soda molecule

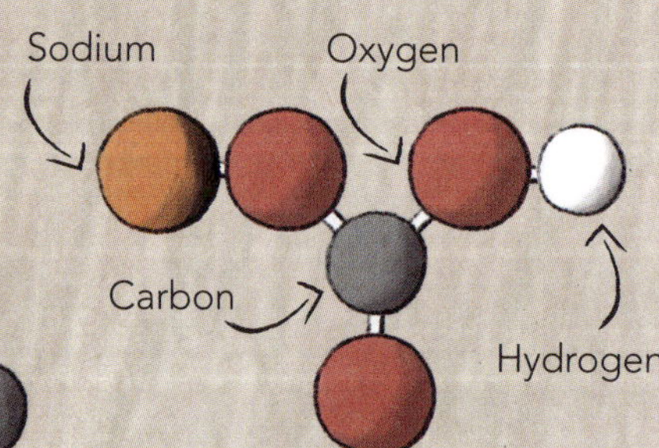

Molecule models

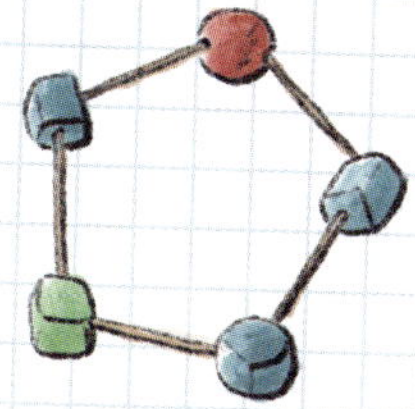

Try making some models of molecules. We've given you some suggestions of everyday items below.

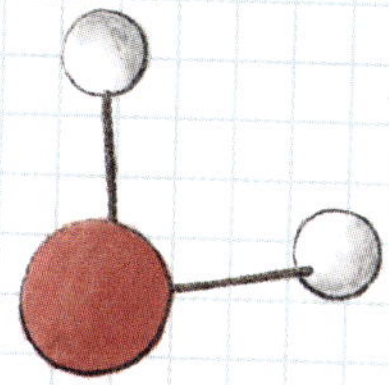

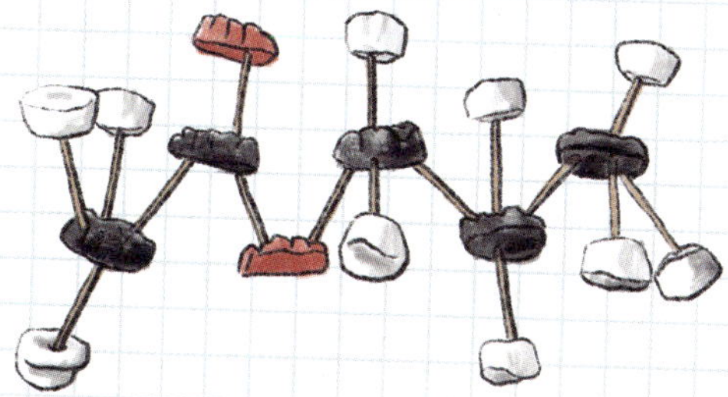

For the atoms, you could use:

Balls of craft clay

Foam craft balls

Jelly candies or sweets

Grapes or berries

For the bonds, you could use:

Cocktail sticks

Matchsticks

Pieces of dry spaghetti

Sections of pipe cleaner or straw

Heading

Can you make models of all the molecules on these pages?

BOING!!!

What makes some materials stretchy, springy, and bouncy?

Springy things

We use lots of stretchy and springy things in everyday life ...

Rubber bands

Diving board

Trampoline

Stretchy fabrics

How it works

These things are elastic because of the way their molecules are arranged.

When you bend or stretch them, they don't break.

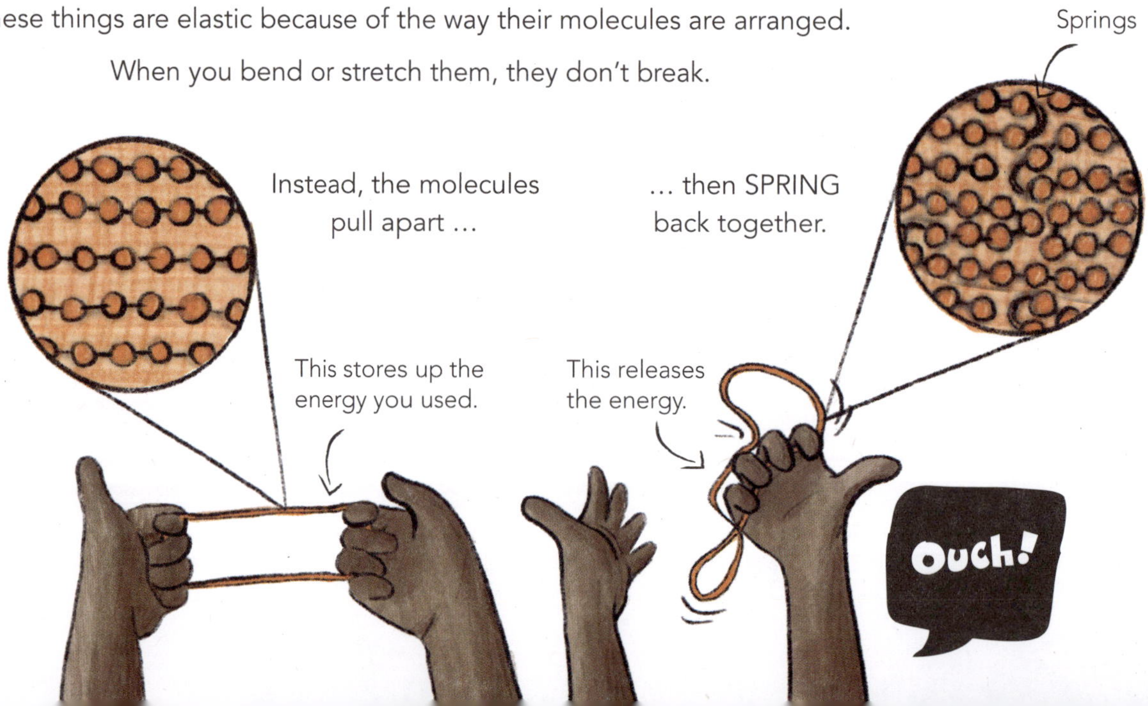

Spoon catapult

You can use the stretchiness of rubber bands to make a mini catapult. You need rubber bands, popsicle or craft sticks, and a teaspoon.

Wrap bands tightly around two sticks to hold them together at one end.

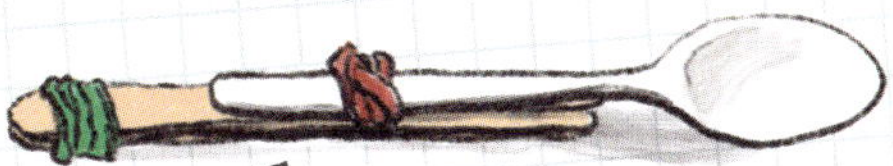

Use bands to attach the spoon to the upper stick.

Tie a stack of 4 sticks together, and put them in between.

Put a crumpled paper ball or mini pom-pom here.

Press down the spoon, stretching the elastic ...

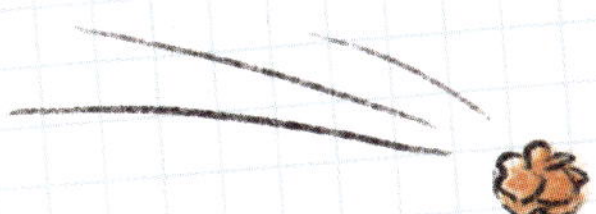

... then let go!

Ready, aim, fire!

Lay this book flat, and use your catapult to aim at the target.

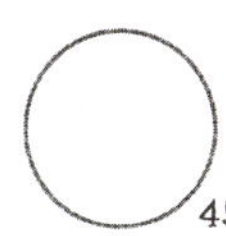

It's elemental!

Elements are pure substances, made of just one type of atom.

Pure gold

For example, gold is an element. It has just one type of atom—gold atoms.

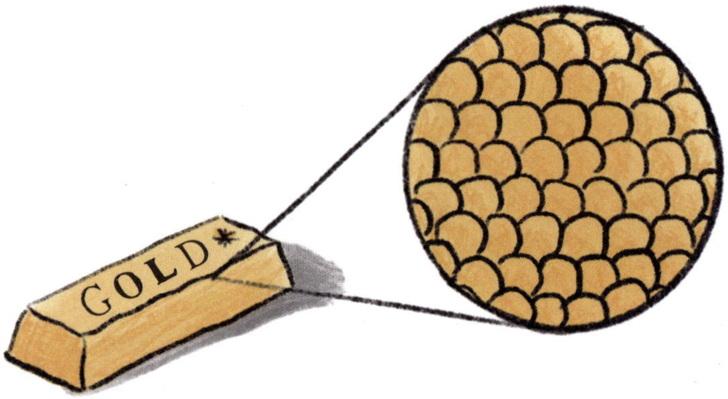

Pure oxygen

Oxygen is an element made of just oxygen atoms.

We breathe oxygen in from the air. But on top of the highest mountains, there's not enough oxygen, so mountaineers take pure oxygen with them.

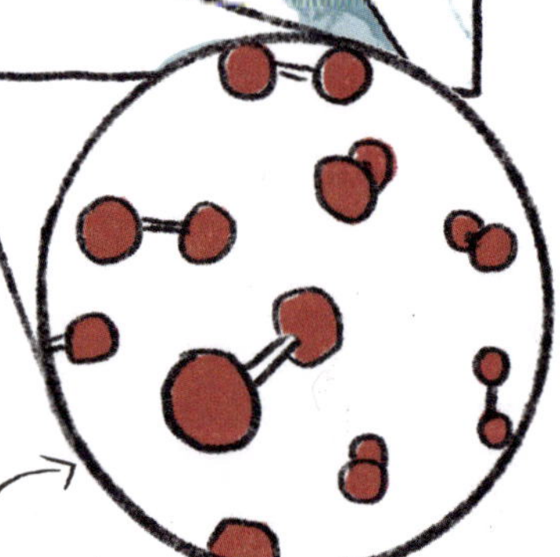

Oxygen molecules are made of oxygen atoms

Elements everywhere!

Look around your home or school, and you should be able to find some elements!

Gold

Gold trinkets such as rings

Silver

Silverware or a trophy

Helium

This gas makes helium balloons float upward.

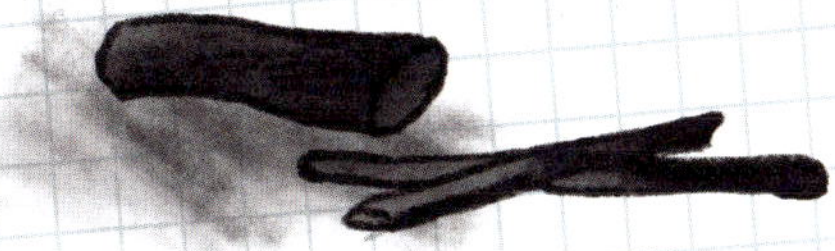

Carbon

A stick of charcoal and the black parts on burned toast are mostly made of carbon.

Diamonds are carbon, too.

Copper

Coins, pipes, pans, or garden wire

Aluminum (also called aluminium)

drink cans

Vitamins and minerals

Ask an adult if you can look at a bottle of multivitamins and minerals, and see if you can spot some elements! Our bodies need them in order to work properly.

You might see:

Calcium	**Magnesium**	**Selenium**
Zinc	**Iron**	**Potassium**

How many elements can you find?

Put an X by them here.

- ☐ Aluminum
- ☐ Calcium
- ☐ Carbon
- ☐ Copper
- ☐ Gold
- ☐ Helium
- ☐ Iron
- ☐ Magnesium
- ☐ Potassium
- ☐ Selenium
- ☐ Silver
- ☐ Zinc

Rock lab

Put your rocks and minerals to the test!

Rock collection

You can test any rocks, pebbles, or minerals, but check with an adult before testing anything that might be precious.

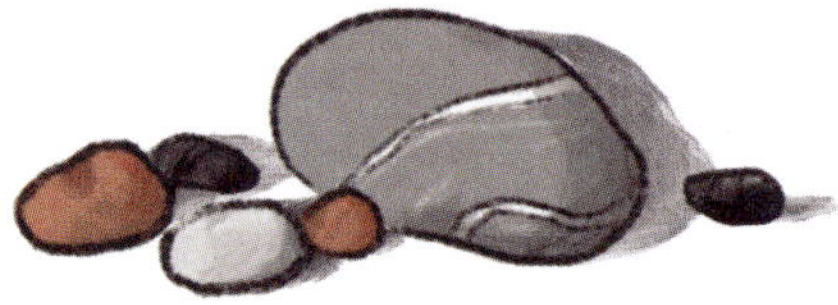

Pebbles from the ground, a path, or parking area

Minerals or crystals from a museum store or toy store

Testing time!

Try these tests!

Does it hold water?

Weigh your rock or mineral using a kitchen scale. Then soak it in a bowl of water for 30 minutes, dry it, and weigh it again.

If it's heavier after soaking, it's a "porous" rock, meaning that it can hold water.

Is it pulled by a magnet?

Does a magnet stick to it?

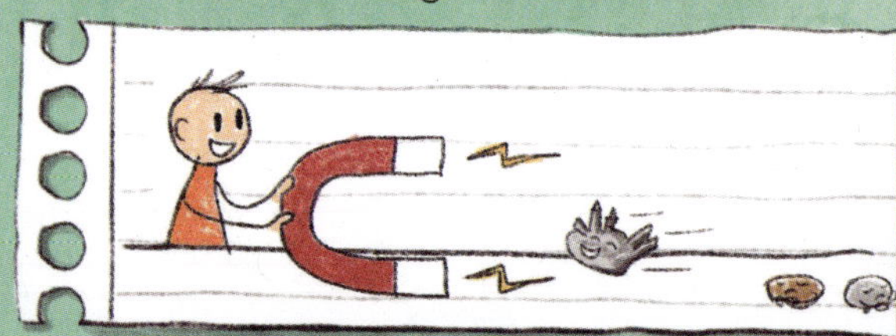

If so, it contains a metal, such as iron.

How hard is it?

Ask an adult for a nail, and try to scratch your rock or mineral with it.

Softer rocks and minerals can be scratched. Harder ones can't!

The fizz test

Put a drop of vinegar or lemon juice on your rock or mineral.

If it fizzes slightly, it's a "calcium carbonate" rock, such as limestone or chalk.

Rock records

Geologists (rock scientists) make notes and sketches of the rocks and minerals they find.

Which is which?

Rocks, stones, and pebbles are made of a mixture of different materials.

Granite

Minerals such as quartz are the same all the way through.

Quartz

Weather watcher

Weather scientists are called meteorologists.
They figure out how to predict the weather—by watching the weather!

Try it yourself

To be a weather scientist, keep track of different kinds of weather for a week.

What to look for

Each day, check what's happening, and make notes.

Wind

How windy is it? Look at trees and plants to see how much they move around, and see how windy it feels when you're outdoors.

Wind

Calm?

Breezy?

✓ Windy?

Very windy?

Rain, snow, or hail?

Water falling from the sky, whether as liquid rain or frozen snow or hail, is called "precipitation."

Precipitation

Rain, snow, or hail? hail

Heavy or light? heavy

Cloudy or clear?

Clouds are made of water that has evaporated into the air from the sea, rivers, and plants.

Cloud

Clear?

Some cloud?

✓ Mostly cloudy?

Totally clouded over?

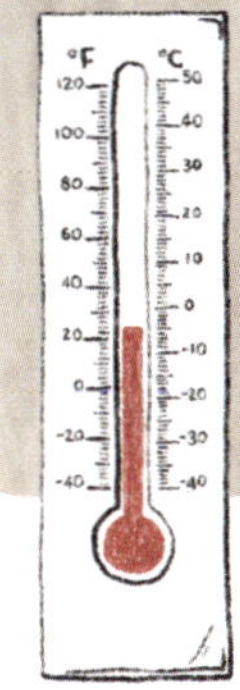

Take the temperature

If you have a thermometer, you can measure the temperature, too.

Leave it outdoors in a shady place, and check it every day at the same time, such as 12 noon.

Temperature

______ °C

______ °F

Weather log

Write down your observations in this weather log, or copy it into a notebook.

	DAY 1	DAY 2	DAY 3	DAY 4	DAY 5	DAY 6	DAY 7
Wind Calm Breezy Windy Very windy!							
Precipitation Rain, snow, or hail Heavy or light							
Cloud Clear Some cloud Mostly cloudy Totally clouded over							
Temperature	____ °C ____ °F	____ °C ____ °F	____ °C ____ °F	____ °C ____ °F	____ °C ____ °F	____ °C ____ °F	____ °C ____ °F
Extra notes:							

Water, water, everywhere!

Floods happen when there's too much water for the land to soak up.

What causes floods?

There are several possible causes ...

Lots of heavy rain

Mountain snow and ice melting

A dam overflowing

Tsunami or storm waves flowing onto the land

Floods and climate change

Global warming makes more water evaporate into the air as a gas.

It turns into more clouds and rain, making floods worse.

Warmer oceans cause stronger cyclones (big, swirling wind storms), with heavy rain and storm waves.

Flood maps

Scientists use flood maps to show which areas of land are at risk of flooding. Check the map to find out whose house is in the flood risk area.

The answer is on page 94!

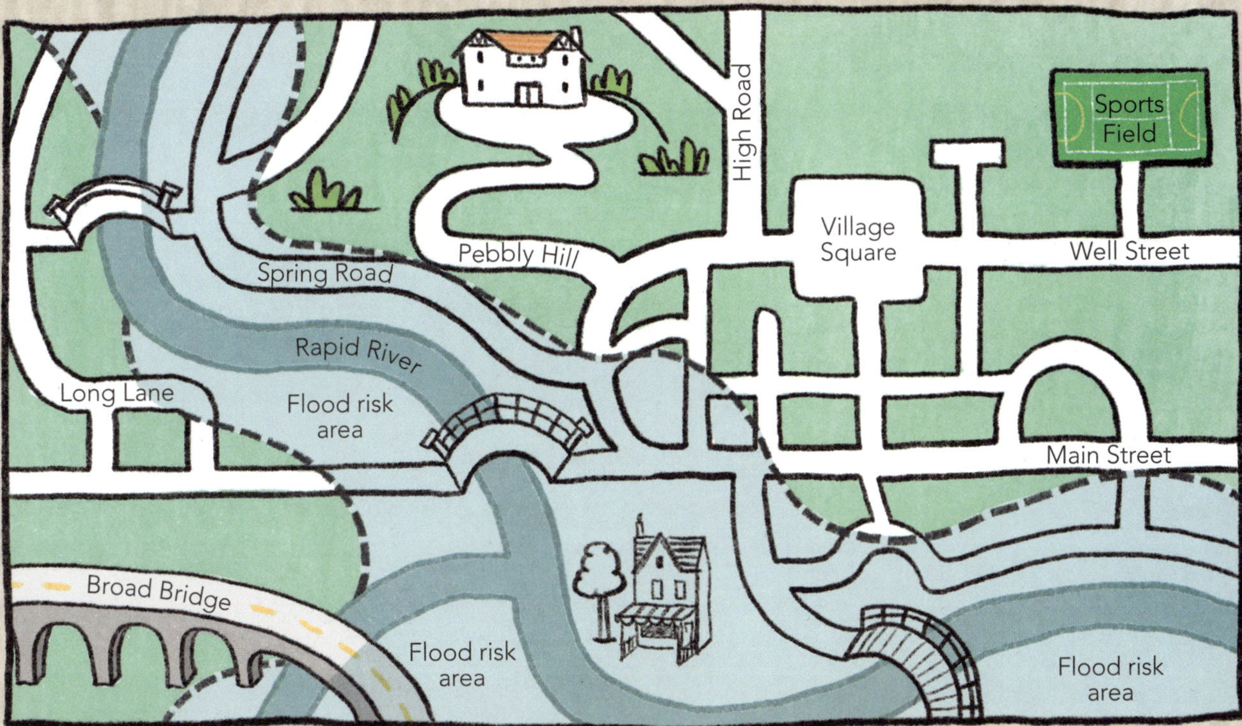

Staying afloat

Which things float—and why?

Take a guess

Collect a bunch of small objects that it's okay to get wet. Things like ...

Coin 

Eraser 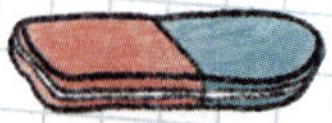

Seashell 

Pebble 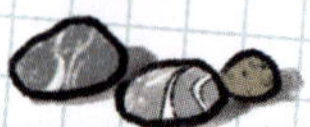

Pumice foot scrubber 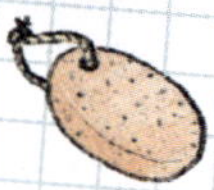

Marble 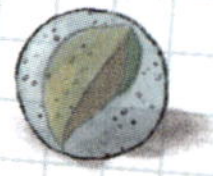

Paper clip 

Pencil 

Foam ball 

Crayon 

Plastic toy brick 

Cork 

Pine cone 

Buttons 

Wooden spoon 

Chocolate or candy 

Grapes or berries 

Sink or float?

Now guess whether each item will float in water. Write down your guesses here.

SINK	FLOAT

The moment of truth!

Then, with an adult to supervise, test the objects in a bowl of water, and see if you were right!

WHAT SANK?	WHAT FLOATED?

How it works

Floating depends on density: how heavy something is for its size. If it's denser than water, the water can't hold it up, and it sinks.

Glass is dense and heavy for its size, so a marble sinks.

But a foam ball the same size is much lighter and floats!

Try this!

If a shape has air inside, that reduces its density, helping it to float.

Try floating a ball of clay.

Then shape it into a boat, and try again!

Spot the germs!

Germs are tiny living things that can cause diseases.

For example, if chickenpox germs invade your body, you can catch chickenpox …

… which makes you feel hot, tired, and sick, and gives you a spotted rash.

There are different types of germs, including:

Bacteria

Each bacterium has only one cell (the tiny units that living things are made of).

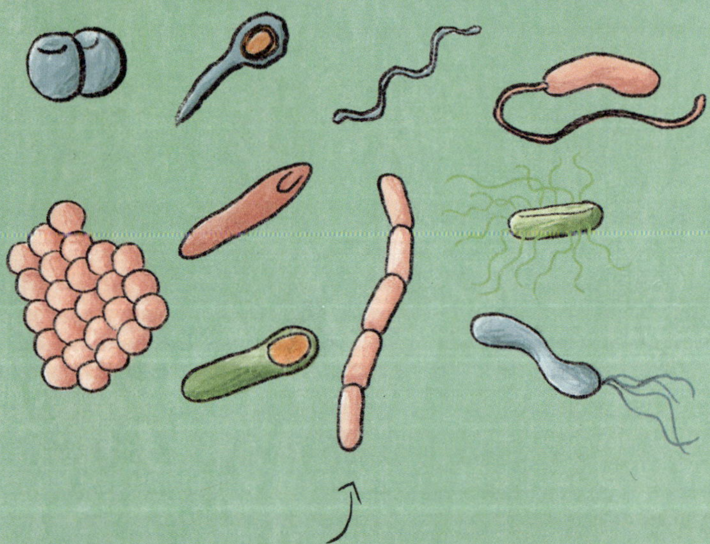

They can be round, sausage-shaped, spiral-shaped and all sorts of other shapes.

Viruses

Viruses are even smaller. They invade cells and force them to make more viruses.

They can look like spiky balls, like this coronavirus.

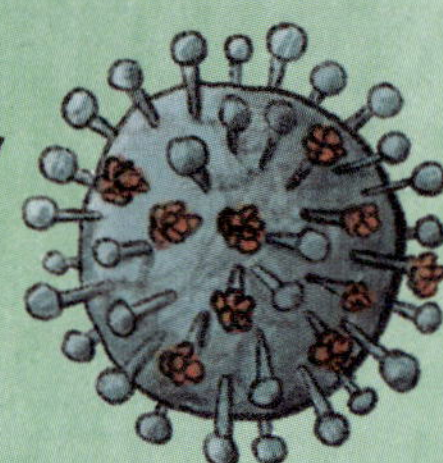

Long strings

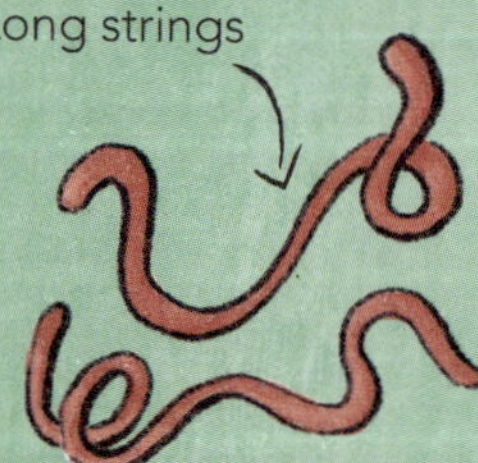

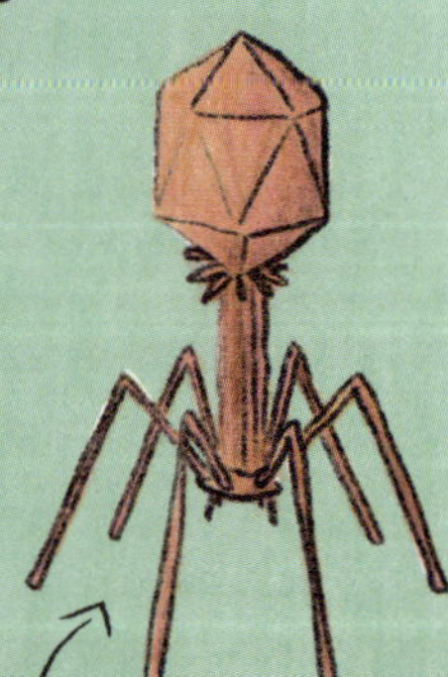

Or weird hexagon "spiders"!

Which do you think are bacteria, and which are viruses?

The answers are on page 94!

Which is which?

Here's a bunch of germs, along with the diseases they cause.

Flu

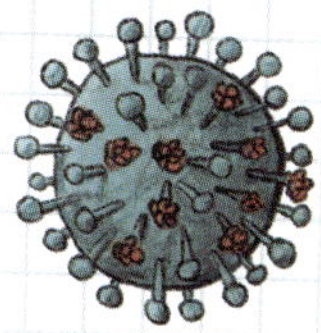

☐ Bacteria
☐ Virus

Strep throat

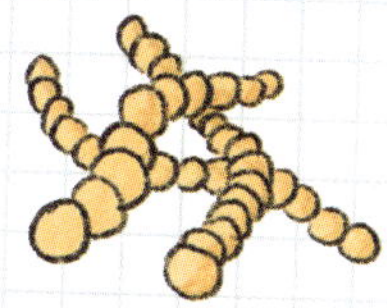

☐ Bacteria
☐ Virus

Tuberculosis (TB)

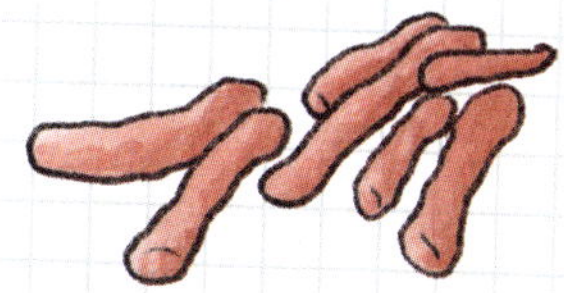

☐ Bacteria
☐ Virus

Cholera

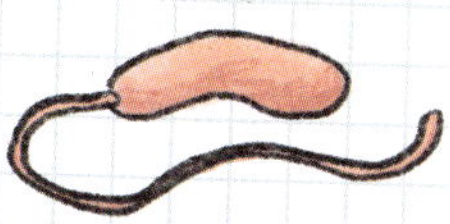

☐ Bacteria
☐ Virus

COVID-19

☐ Bacteria
☐ Virus

Food poisoning

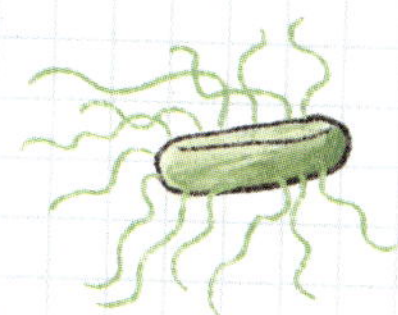

☐ Bacteria
☐ Virus

Ebola

☐ Bacteria
☐ Virus

Jazz up the pics!

Scientists use powerful microscopes to photograph germs, but the pictures are black and white. To make the pictures easier to see, they make them bright and vibrant, like below.

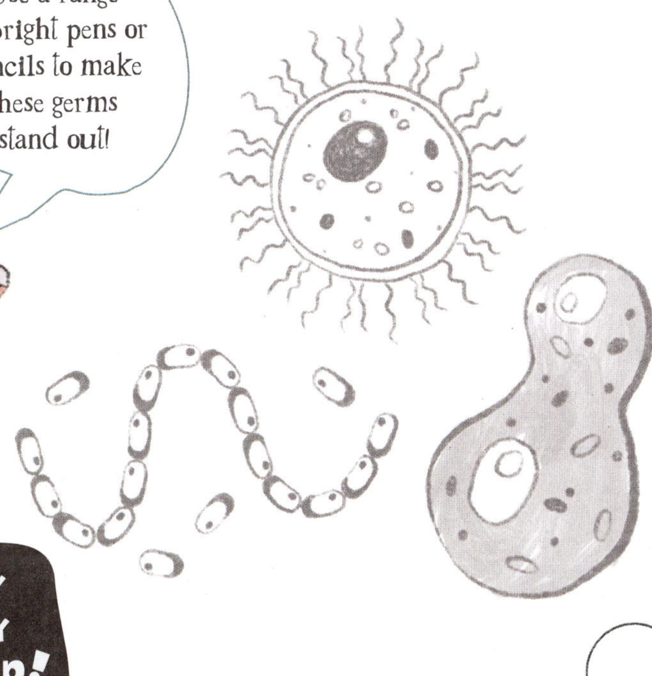

One becomes many

All living things can reproduce, meaning that they can have babies or make copies of themselves. Even bacteria!

Splitting in two

When a bacterium wants to reproduce, it simply gets bigger, then divides into two new bacteria. Like this ...

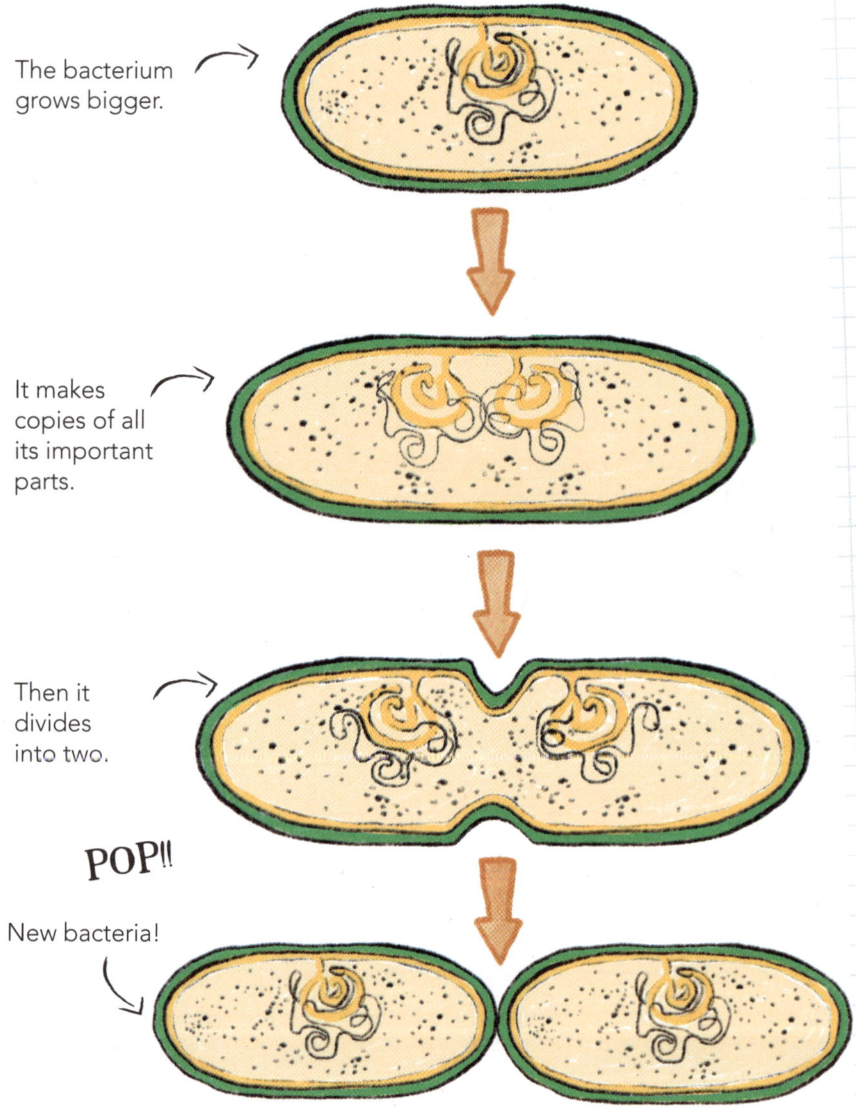

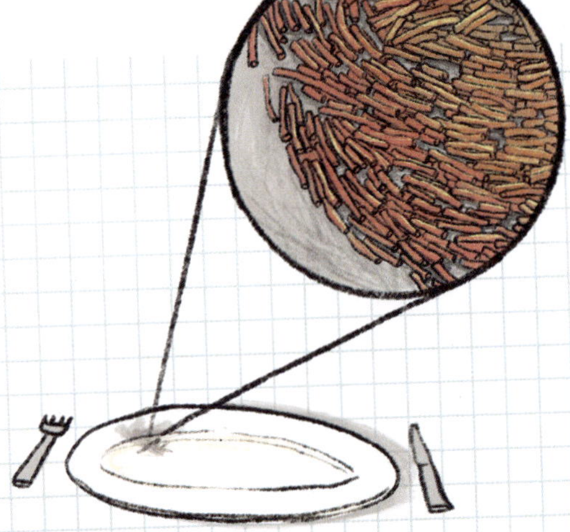

They're multiplying!

As long as bacteria have enough food, they'll keep growing and dividing, making more and more and MORE bacteria! In just a few hours, one bacterium can become a million or more.

Super-speedy

To see just how quickly bacteria can multiply, try this!

Here's one bacterium.

Now it's split into two.

Now each of *them* has split into two, so there are four!

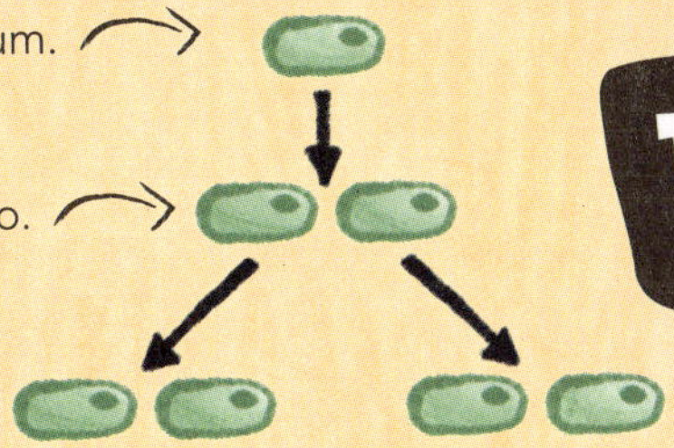

Keep going ...

How long is it until there are too many bacteria to fit in?

Fossil finders

Long ago, there were all kinds of creatures that no longer exist. How do we know? Fossils!

Stone bones

Fossils often look like old bones, seashells, or other animal parts, made of stone.

T. rex skull

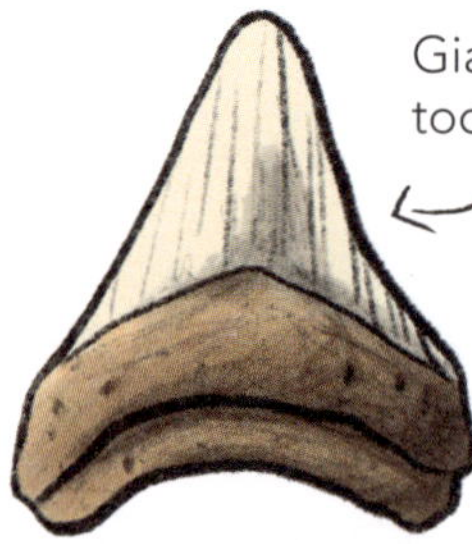

Giant shark tooth

Trilobite

How it happens

Fossils can form when bones or other body parts get buried, then slowly dissolve away.

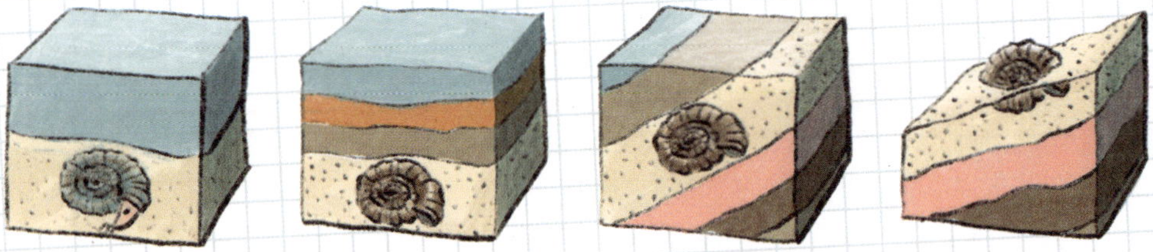

Water filled with minerals soaks into the spaces.

Rock builds up in the same shape—and you get a fossil!

Sometimes, a plant or animal gets squashed.

Minerals from its body leave a mark called a carbon film fossil.

Trace fossils are marks or footprints that have been fossilized.

Even a poop can become a fossil!

Fossil jigsaw puzzles

Some fossils come all in one piece, like this ammonite.

Others are skeletons made up of separate fossil bones. Paleontologists, have to fit them together.

Build a Brachiosaurus

Paleontologists have dug up a bunch of fossil dinosaur bones.

They think it's a Brachiosaurus, a ginormous dinosaur that looked like this.

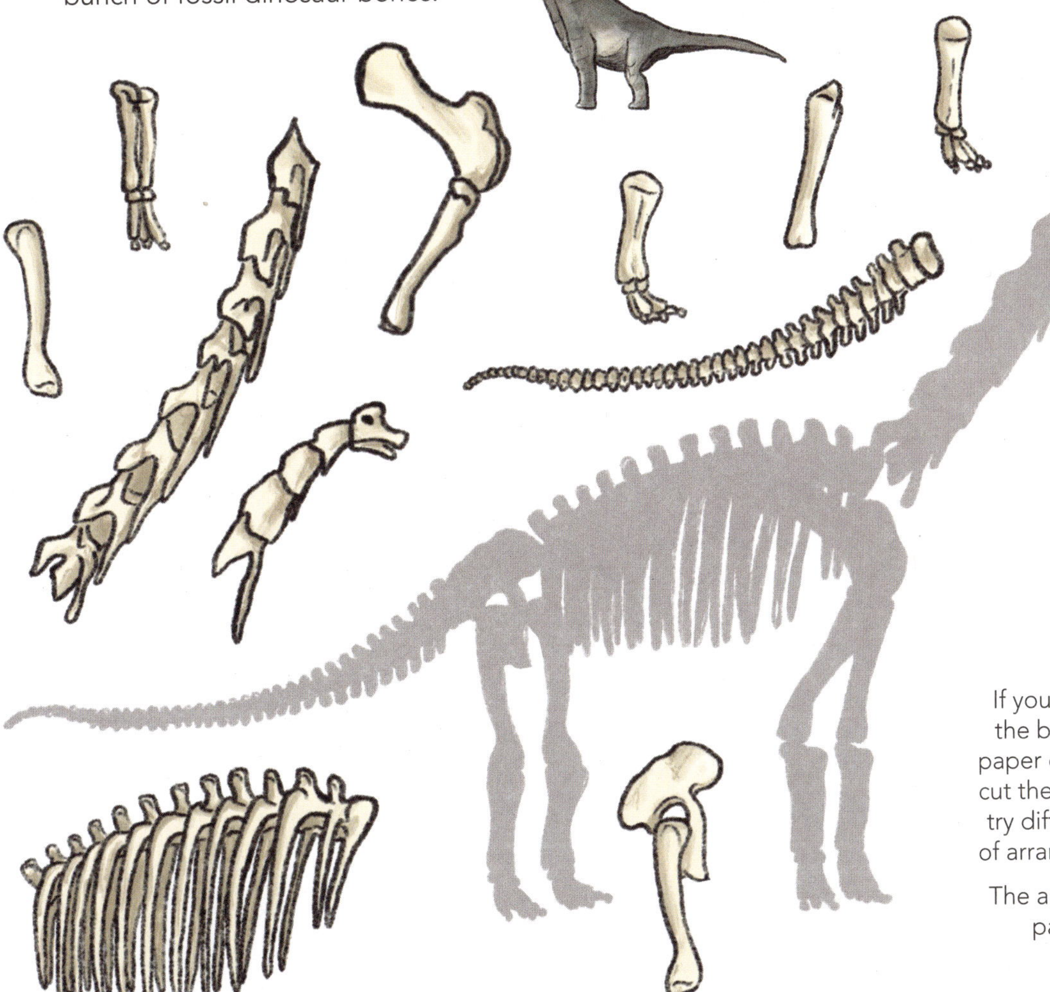

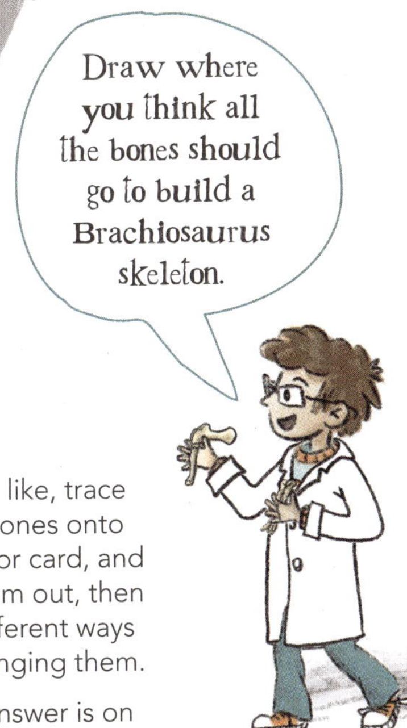

If you like, trace the bones onto paper or card, and cut them out, then try different ways of arranging them.

The answer is on page 94.

Egg-Stra Strength!

You might think of eggs as very delicate and easy to break, but they can actually be very strong.

Safe to sit on!

But if you press steadily on an egg, it's doesn't break easily.

This keeps eggs safe when birds sit on them to keep them warm.

Mighty eggshells

This experiment shows how strong eggshells can be.

See how much weight you can add before they collapse. It might surprise you!

Egg buildings

Architects have used egg shapes to make strong domes for buildings.

Design your own egg-shaped building here:

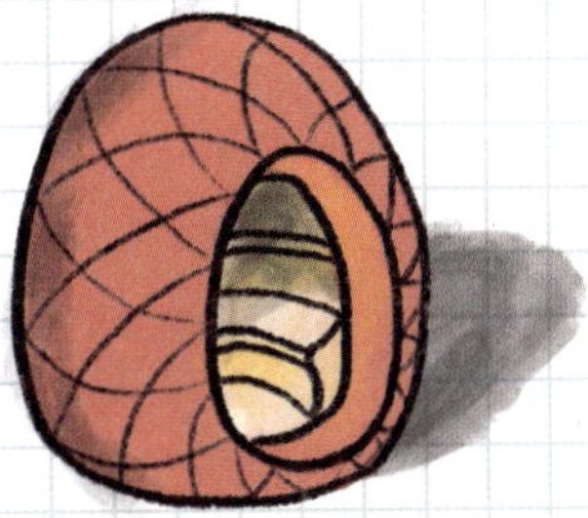

The tree of life

Scientists sort living things into different groups, or "branches"—like the branches of a tree!

Evolution tree

The first living things were tiny, single-celled creatures (a bit like the bacteria on page 56).

Over time, living things changed, or evolved. More and more new species formed, branching off from older species. We can show this as a tree diagram, like this.

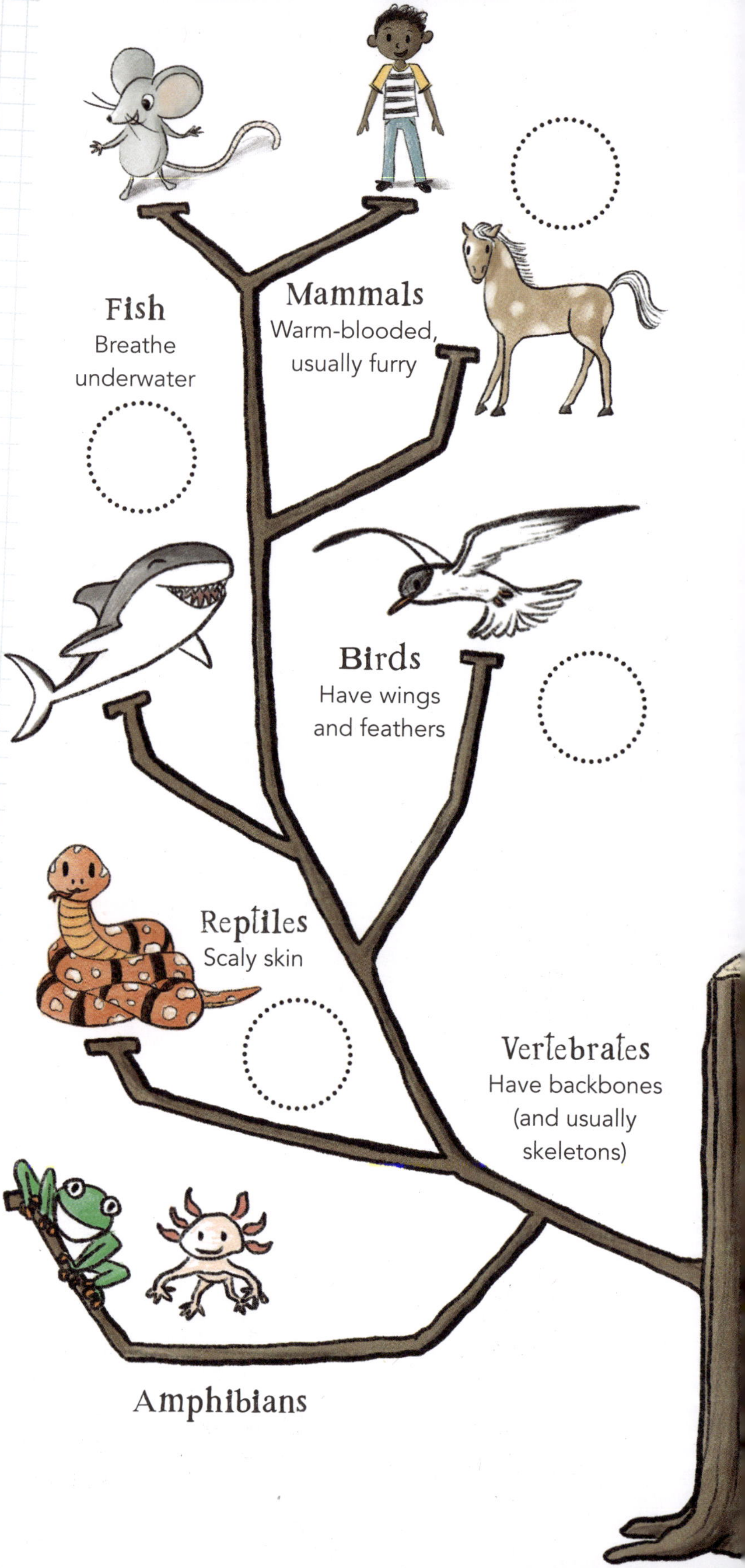

Sort them out!

Can you match these living things to the spaces in the tree?

When you've found the right place, draw the creature there.

- Cat
- Piranha
- Toadstool
- Sunflower
- Tarantula
- Lizard
- Parrot
- Earthworm

What are flowers for?

Have you ever wondered why flowers are beautiful and smell nice?

Making seeds

Flowers are the parts of a plant that make seeds.

They release a yellow powder called pollen.

If pollen lands on another flower of the same type, that flower can make seeds.

The flower grows into a fruit with seeds inside.

How animals help

Pollen can blow in the wind, but it can also travel on animals, such as bees.

When bees fly from flower to flower, they take pollen with them.

That's helpful for flowers! So, to make bees visit, they provide sweet nectar for the bees to eat and have bright petals and sweet scents to help bees find them.

Take a look!

Next time you see bees visiting flowers, watch them closely. You might see the grains of pollen stuck to their fur.

Flowers for bees

Use this space to design and draw some flowers that bees will LOVE!

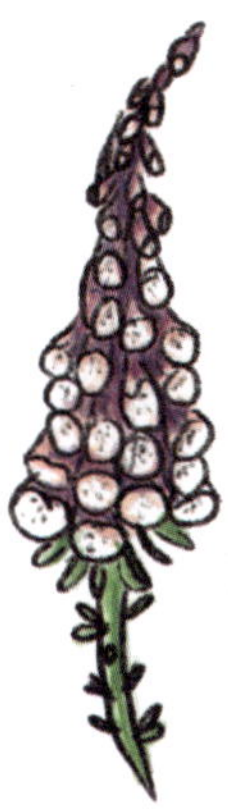

Written in the rings

The rings inside a tree trunk can reveal all kinds of things!

Why do trees have rings?

Trees grow faster in the spring and more slowly in late summer. That makes a ring each year, made up of bands of lighter and darker wood.

That means we can tell a tree's age from the number of rings in its trunk.

Did you know?

Not all trees have rings!

Some tropical areas don't have very different seasons, so trees there don't always have rings.

Read the tree

Here's another tree trunk with lots of rings. Take a look, and find out what it has to say!

How old was this tree? ________

Find two forest fires.

How long ago were they?

____

____

Can you spot an insect outbreak?

You can find the answers on page 94.

Incredible journeys

Some animals go on huge long-distance journeys. It's called migrating.

Why?

Usually, it's to find food, to have babies, or to avoid weather they don't like. For example ...

Salmon lay their eggs in mountain streams.

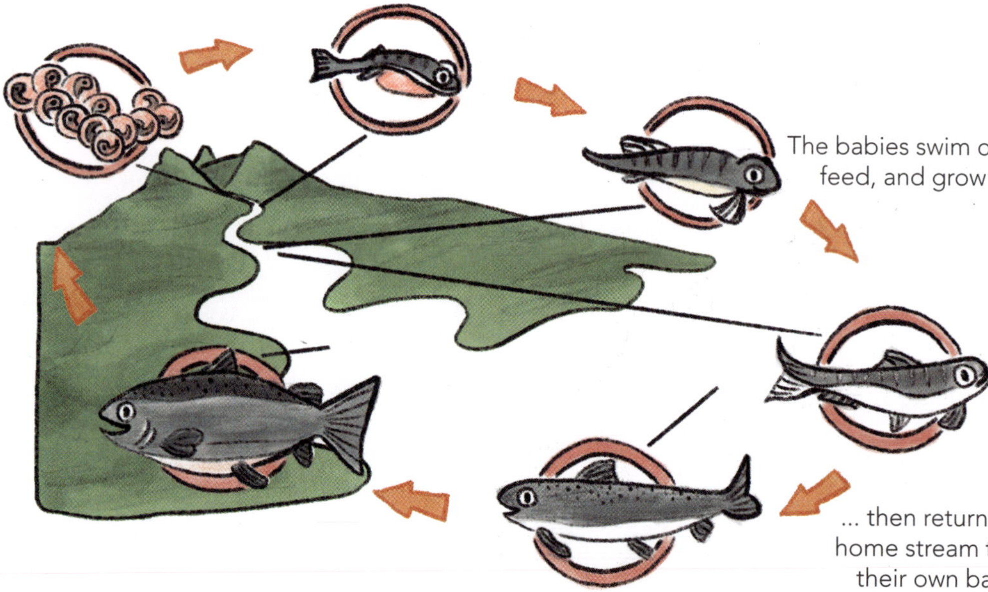

The babies swim out to sea, feed, and grow big ...

... then return to their home stream to have their own babies.

In a lifetime, a salmon travels up to 11,000 km (7,000 mi)!

Long distance champion

The amazing Arctic tern flies from the Antarctic to the Arctic and back every-single year, so that it can spend the summer in both places. It flies up to 71,000 km (44,000 mi) each year.

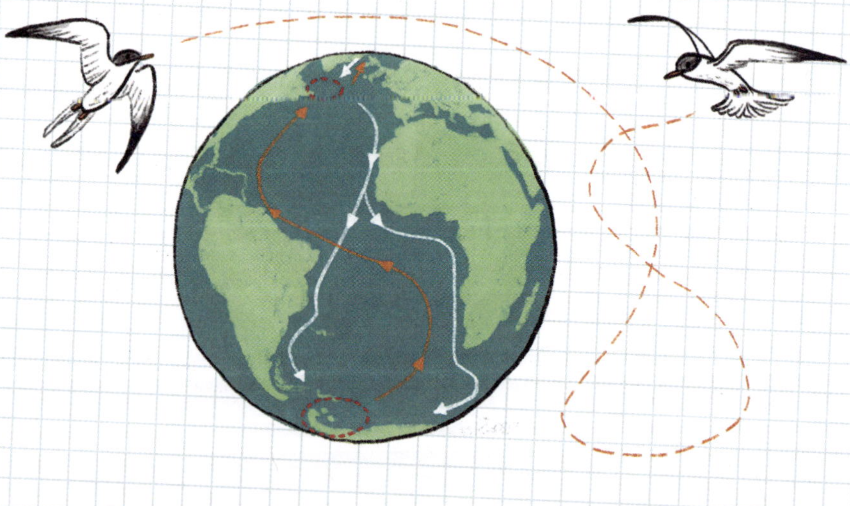

That's up to 2.4 MILLION km (1.5 million mi) in its lifetime!

Migration maps

Scientists sometimes attach tracking devices to animals and make maps of their travels.

Use different pens or pencils to draw these animal journeys on the map.

Monarch butterfly

Saskatchewan, Canada to Mexico

Leatherback turtle

Across the Pacific Ocean from Indonesia to Oregon, USA

Humpback whale

Antarctica to Costa Rica—and back!

Living together

Living things don't live alone! They depend on other living things.

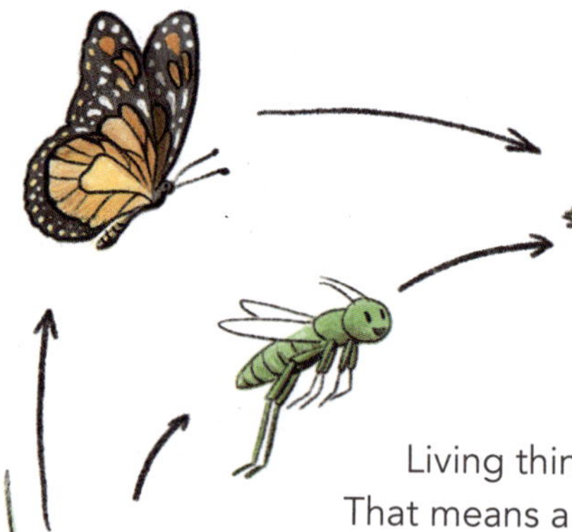

Ecosystems

Living things are found in ecosystems. That means a group of living things, together with their habitat, or the place where they live.

Grass and flowers

get eaten by

Grasshoppers and butterflies

which get eaten by

Small birds

which get eaten by

Eagles

This sequence is called a "food chain."

Food webs

And in most ecosystems, there are lots of food chains, which form a "food web."

Here's a food web in a desert ecosystem.

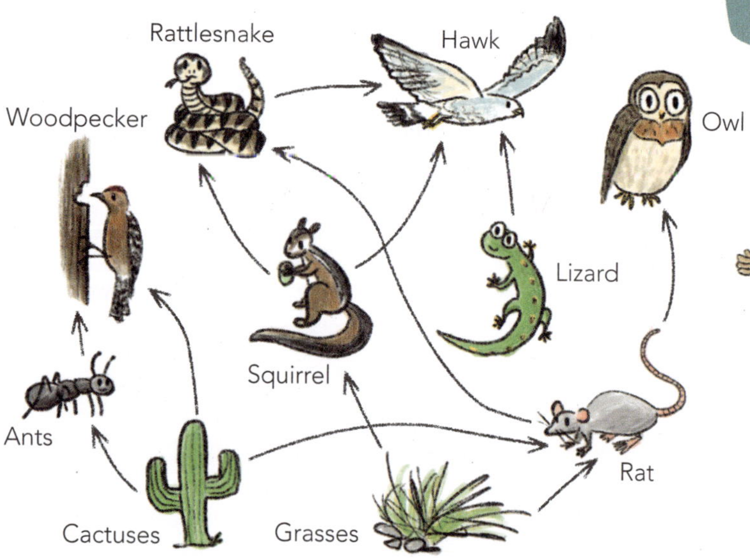

It's a balance!

Everything in an ecosystem is part of a delicate balance.

Who eats who?

This shallow sea food web is empty! Can you figure out what goes where?

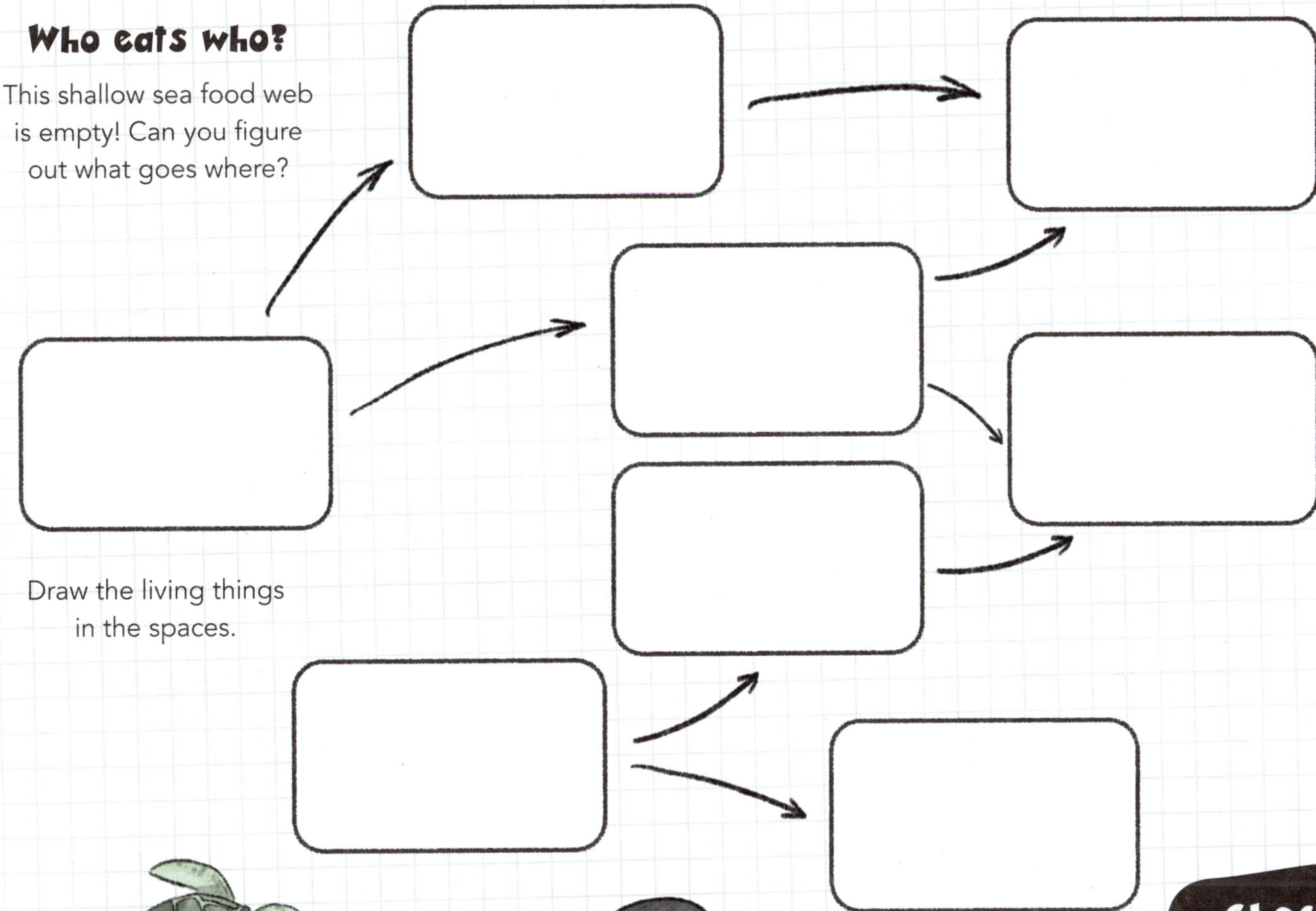

Draw the living things in the spaces.

Weaving a web

Using sticky silk thread they make inside their bodies, spiders weave beautiful webs.

How it works

A spider starts by letting a thread of silk drift across a gap to make a bridge thread.

It makes more threads around the sides and uses anchor threads to attach the web to its surroundings.

It adds threads coming out from the middle, like the spokes of a wheel.

Then it moves around in a circle, spinning a spiral to complete the web.

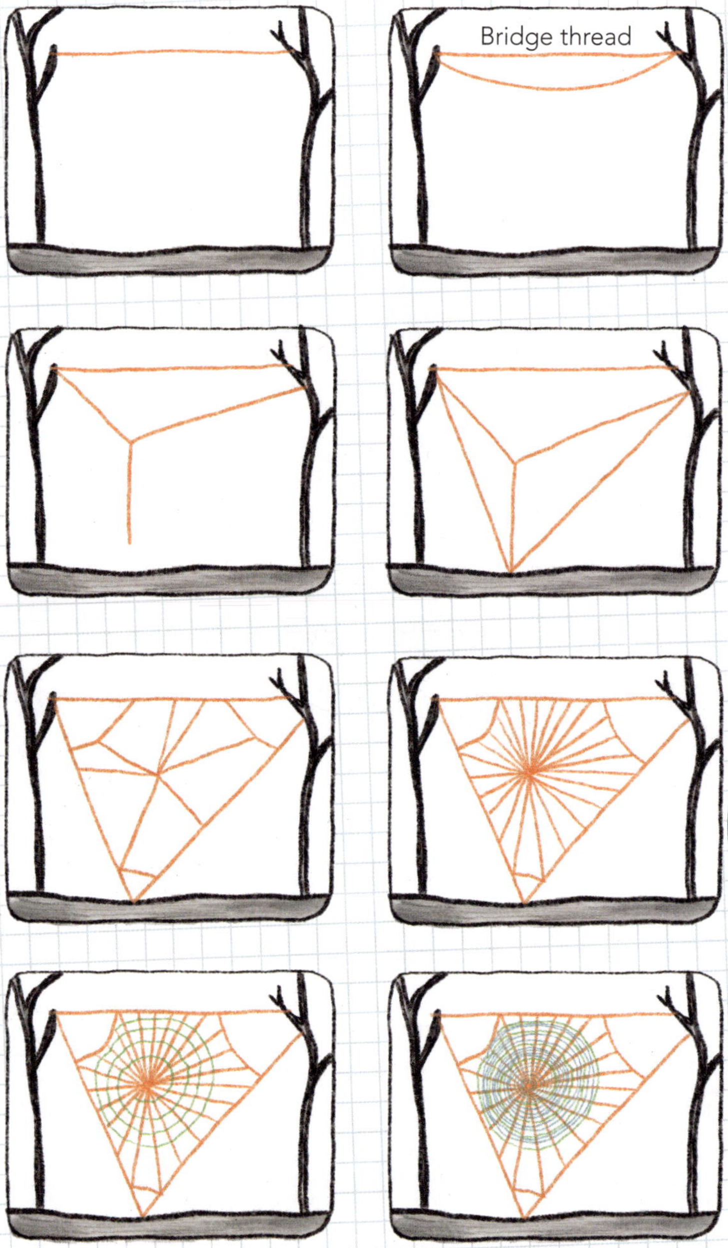

Drawing a web

Draw your own webs by copying the spiders' method!

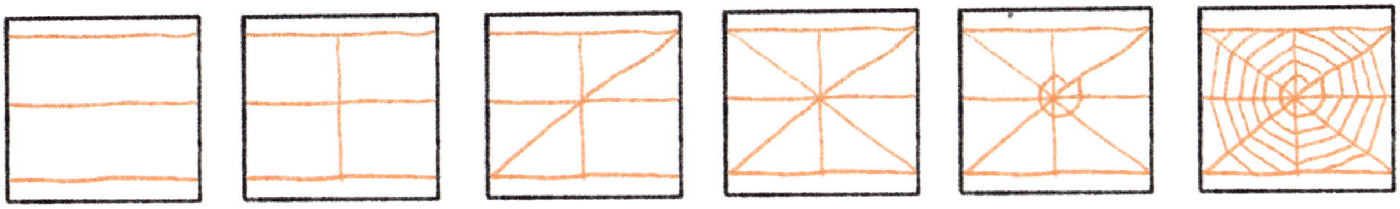

Try drawing a big spiderweb here.

Now weave a web!

You can make a real web, too, using string or knitting yarn.

Tie it between bushes or across a doorway. (Ask permission first!)

Where one thread crosses another, tie a knot to hold them in place.

Speedy Signals

When you see something, how fast can you react to it? Test yourself!

Nerve cells

Our brains contain cells called nerve cells, or neurons.

When we think or make decisions, the neurons are passing signals to each other.

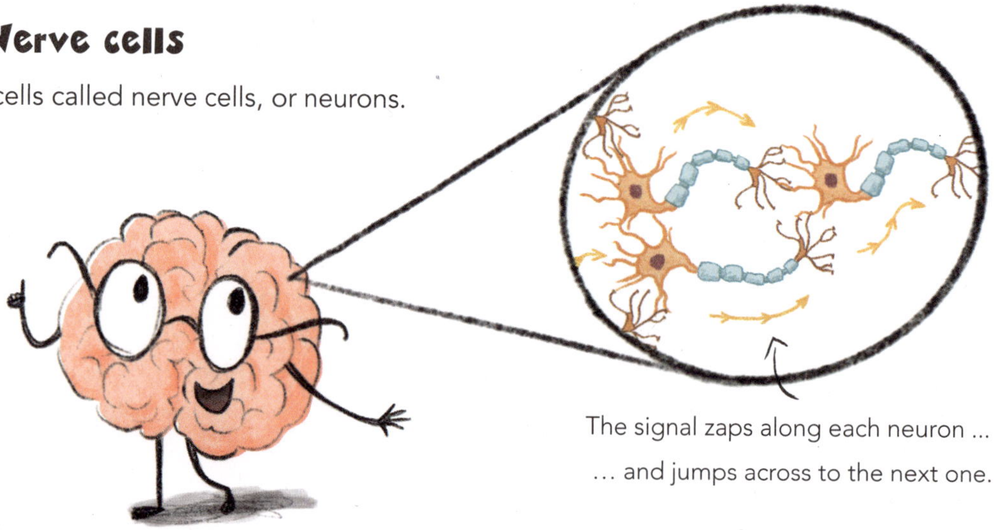

The signal zaps along each neuron ...

... and jumps across to the next one.

Senses and Signals

We also have nerve cells reaching out from our brains to all around our bodies.

They pick up signals from your senses, and take them to your brain.

Then they take messages from your brain to your muscles to make you move!

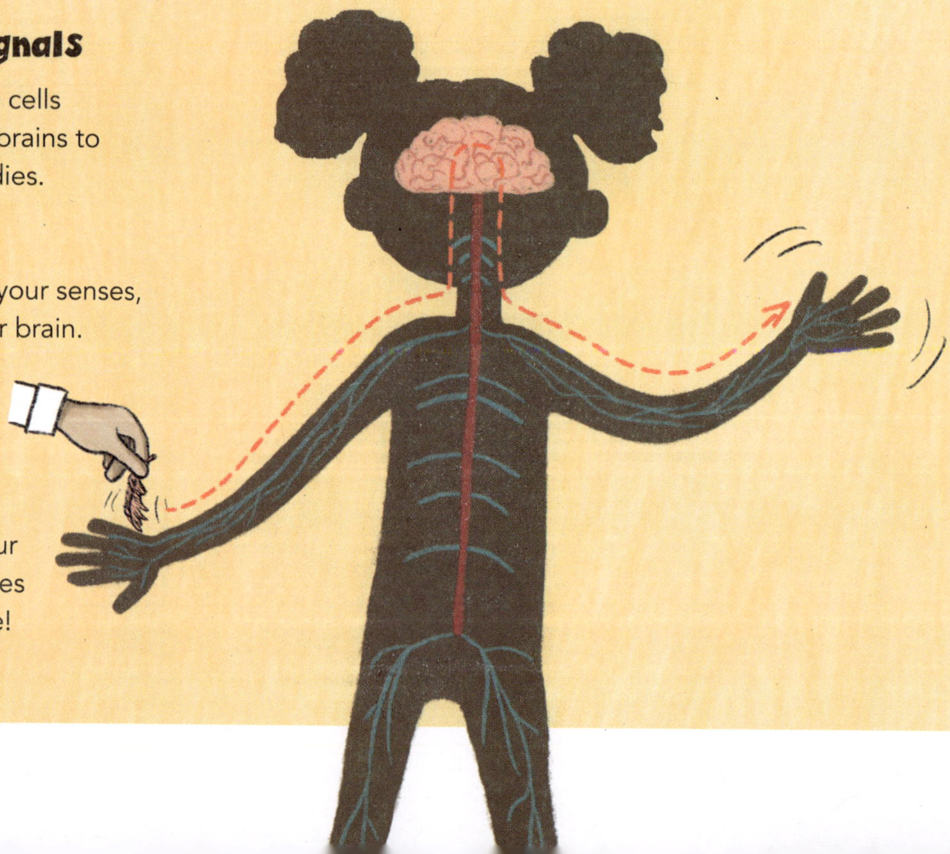

The ruler test

Here's another experiment to try, this time using a ruler.

Ask a friend to hold up a ruler like this, with the lower numbers at the bottom.

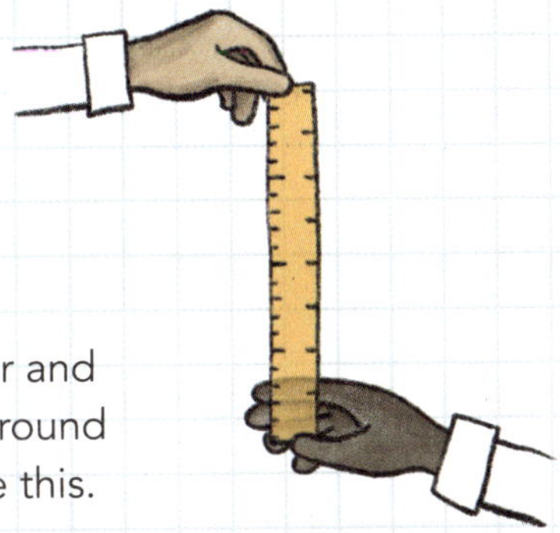

Hold your finger and thumb loosely around the bottom, like this.

Ask your friend to drop the ruler without warning.

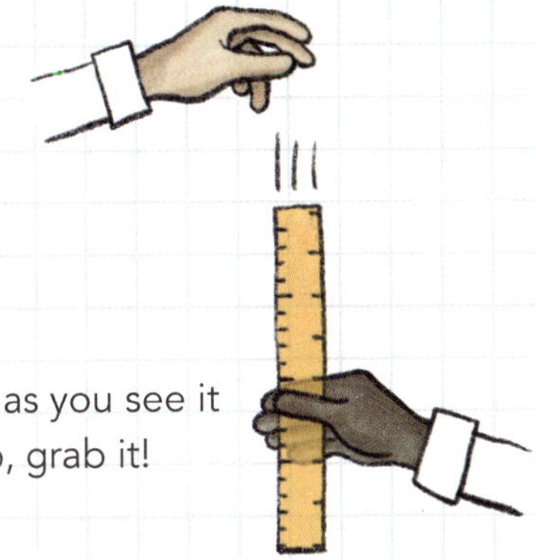

As soon as you see it drop, grab it!

The number your thumb lands on will give you a score.

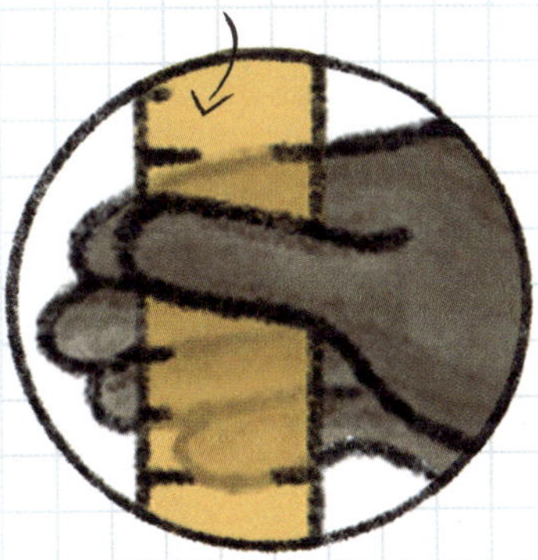

The lower the number, the faster the signals zoomed to and from your brain!

NAME	SCORE

TIME	SCORE
Just woke up	
Lunchtime	
Afternoon	
Bedtime	

You're a tube!

We have a tunnel all the way through our insides!

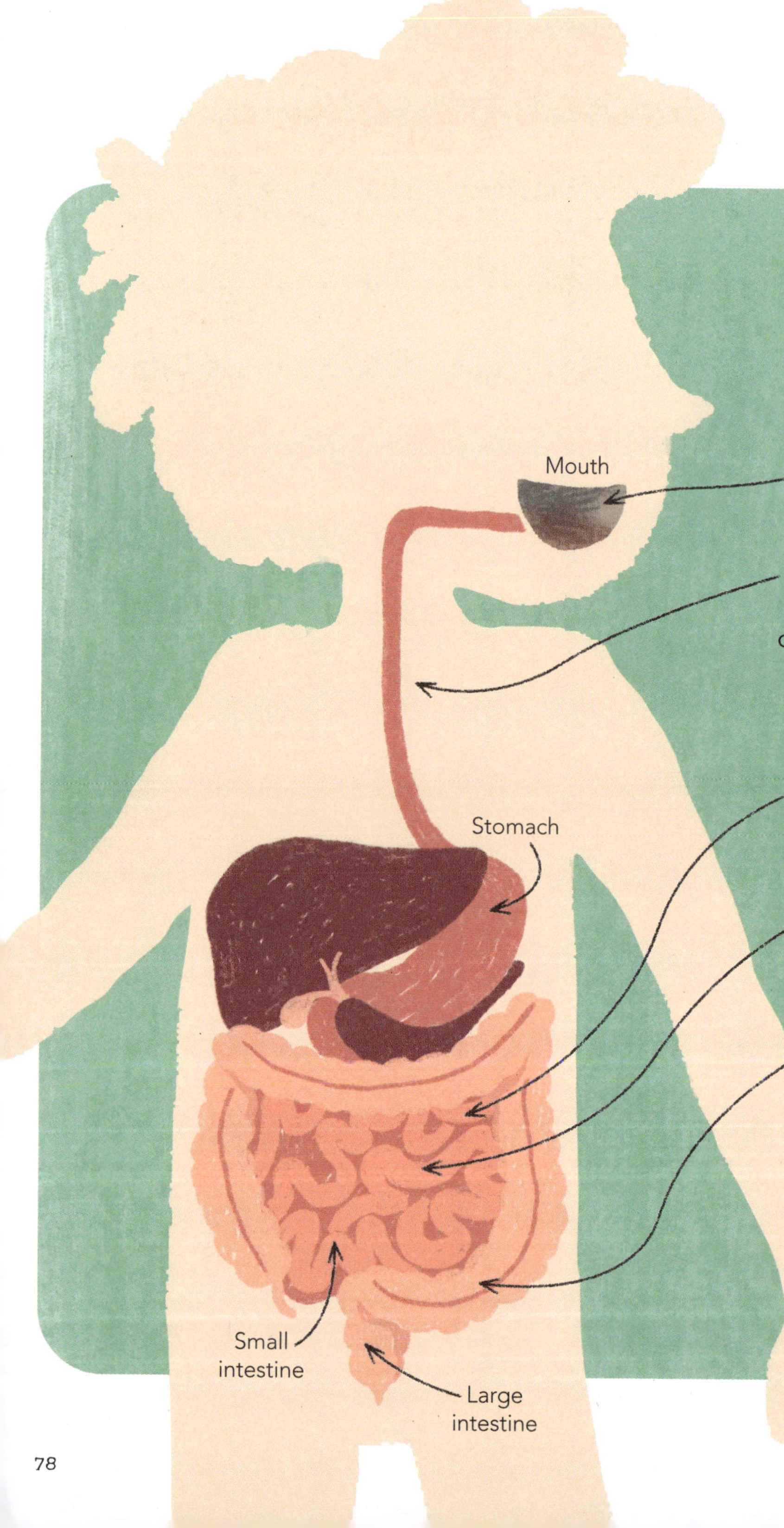

Food in ... waste out

This tunnel is called the digestive system.

It starts with your mouth, which you use for eating and drinking.

After chewing your food, you swallow it, and it goes down this tube, called the oesophagus into your stomach. There, it gets mushed into a soupy liquid.

Then it goes into tubes, called the intestines.

The small intestine soaks up all the useful chemicals from the food.

The large intestine collects what's left over and turns it into lumps of waste—otherwise known as poop! They come out when you go to the toilet.

How long?

As you can see, these tubes are not a straight line. They're all coiled up, especially the small intestine. So how long is your digestive system?

Here's how to find out!

Measure it!

You'll need a tape measure and a calculator! First, measure your height and write it down.

Then do the calculations.

Your height = ____________

Mouth to stomach:
1/4 of your height = ____________ long

Stomach:
the same size as your fist = ____________ long

Small intestine:
3 X your height = ____________ long

Large intestine:
9/10 of your height = ____________ long

Add them up all up to
find the total length. = ____________ long

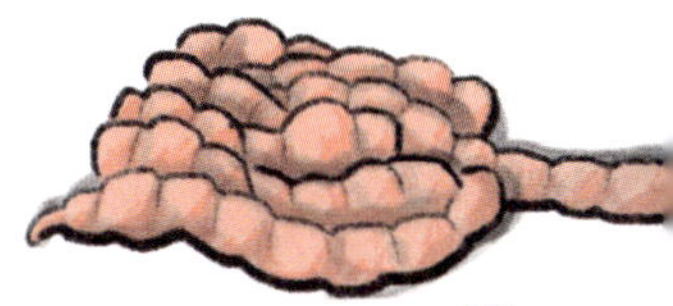

Find your heartbeat

Your heat beats to pump blood around your body.

Pumping blood

This is a very important job—because blood carries oxygen, food, water, and other important things to every part of the body.

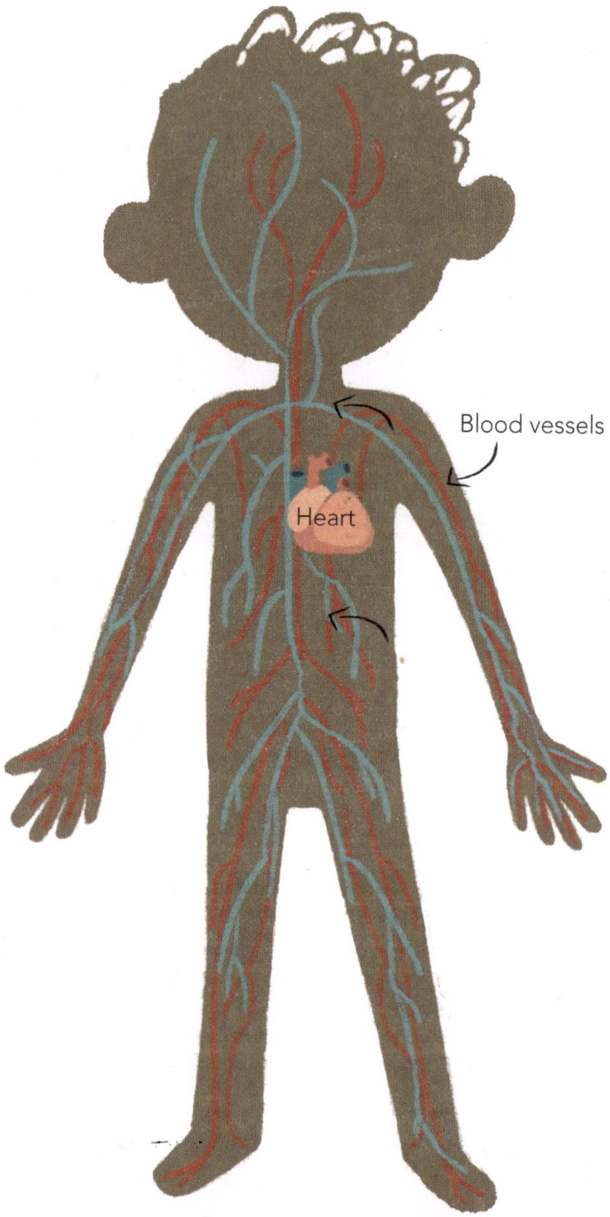

To pump blood, the heart SQUEEZES hard. Each squeeze pushes the blood along and makes a heartbeat, or "pulse."

Where to find it

Here's how to find your pulse.

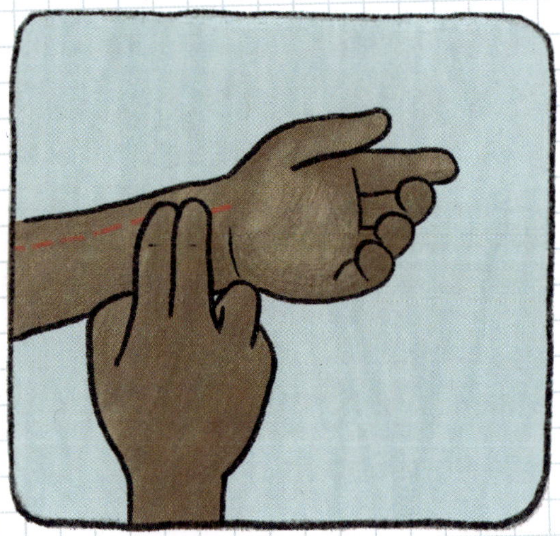

Turn one hand palm-upward.

Place the fingers of your other hand on your wrist, just up from the thumb.

You should feel your pulse!

BUMP! BUMP! BUMP!

Fast and slow

Your heartbeat speeds up and slows down in different situations.

When you're moving fast, your heat beats faster, too, to deliver extra oxygen to your muscles.

It also speeds up if you're scared!

When you're asleep, or very relaxed, your heartbeat is at its slowest.

Pulse rate

Your pulse rate is how many times your heart beats per minute.
Use a clock with a second hand, or a timer, to count the beats in one minute.

Measure it in different situations. Is it fast or slow?

ACTIVITY	PULSE RATE
Just after waking up	
After doing star jumps (or other exercise) for 30 seconds	
Watching TV (funny)	
Watching TV (scary)	

Surprising eyes

Our eyes help us see by detecting light
—but we need our brains to help!

Two eyes

Why have two eyes?
It means that you have a spare if one gets damaged.

Two eyes see things from slightly different angles.
This helps your brain to tell how far away things are.

A hole in your hand!

As your two eyes see slightly different things, your brain has to blend them together. Try this to **see** for yourself!

1. You need a cardboard tube from a roll of kitchen paper or foil.

2. Put it over one eye, and hold your hand next to the tube in front of the other eye, like this.

3. You'll see a hole in your hand!

This happens because your brain combines the views from both eyes.

Afterimage

A part at the back of your eye, called the retina, detects light. It can store information for a while, making an "afterimage" of what you have seen.

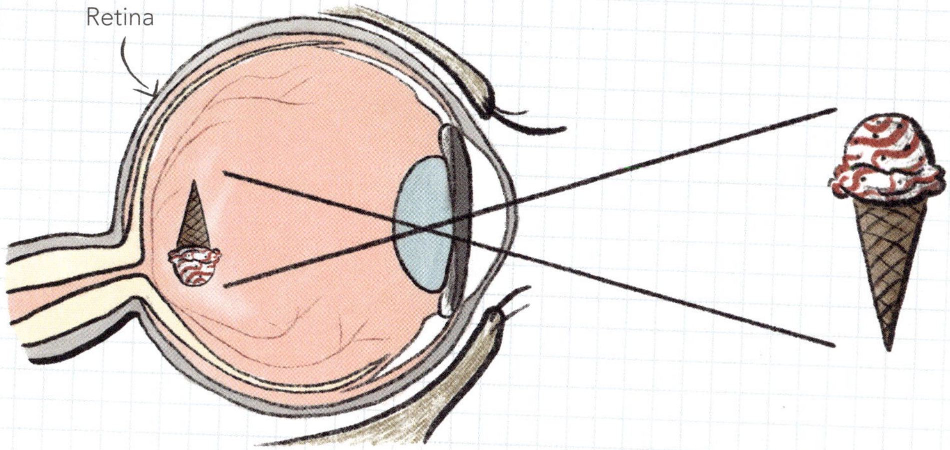

Try this!

Stare at the dot in the middle of this picture for 30 seconds.

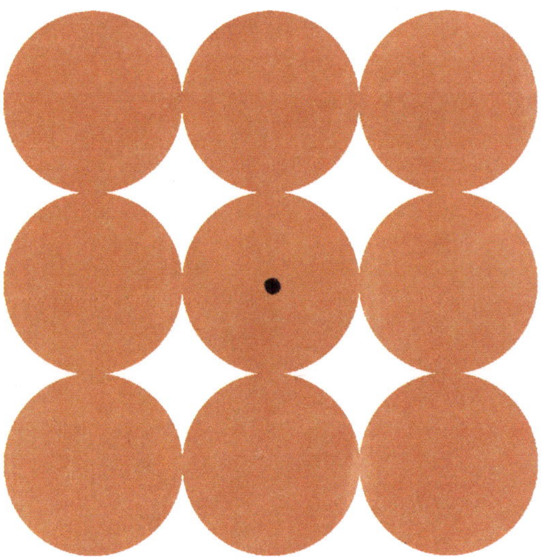

Then look at the white area.

Blind Spot

Each of your eyes has a blind spot where it can't see anything!

Why?

The retina in each eye has a spot where it can't detect light. It's where the retina is connected to the brain.

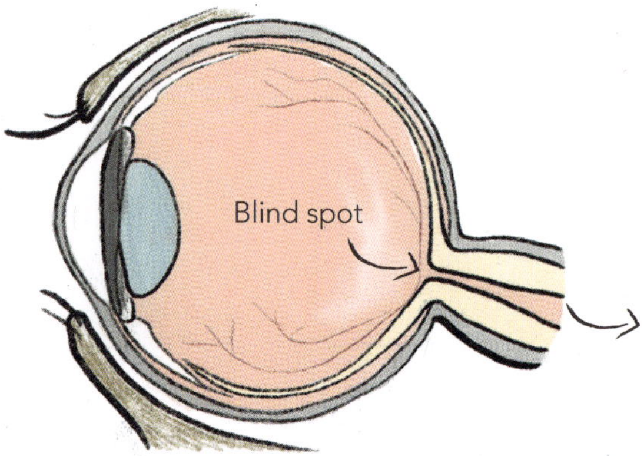

Filling the gap

If you could see your blind spots, they would be blurry areas that would always appear in your field of vision.

But you don't!
Your two eyes "fill in" for each other's blind spots.

Spot the blind spot!

Even with one eye shut, you STILL can't see the blind spot, because your brain fills in the gap. But you can find it. Here's how!

Cover your left eye.

With your right eye, look at the cross. Don't look away!

Move your head slowly closer to the page, then away again.

At some point, the dot will vanish!

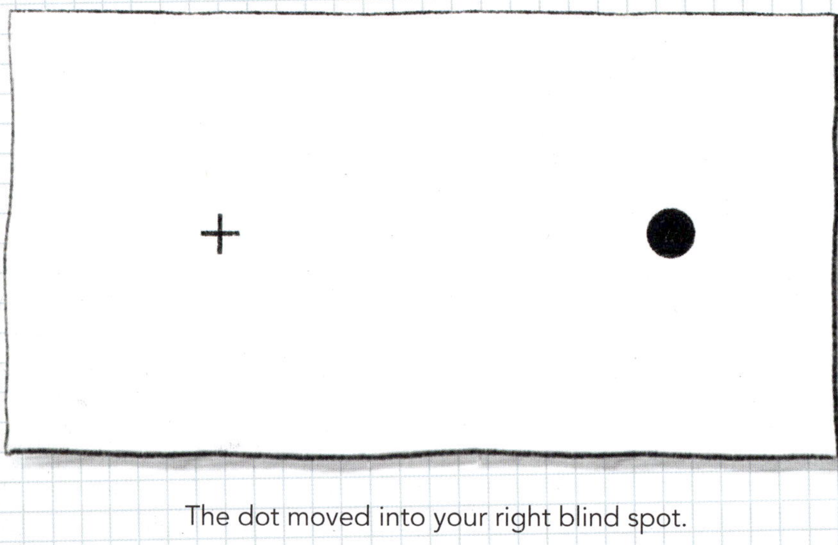

The dot moved into your right blind spot.

Your brain filled the gap with white paper!

Pattern Filler

Your brain will even fill the gap with a pattern. Try this!

When you can't see the [orange] dot, your brain fills the gap with a [blue] one!

Here are some more:

Design your own blind spot test with any pattern around the dot.

Which way around?

Look in a mirror, and you see yourself ... but the other way around!

Why?

The mirror reflects your left side on the left and your right side on the right. Try it, and see!

You just look the other way around from how you do in photos, because a photo shows you as others see you.

Ambigram challenge

A natural ambigram is a word—such as "bud"—that looks the same when reflected.

How many natural ambigrams can you think of?

Write them down, then check whether they work by reflecting them in a mirror.

You could challenge a friend to see who can come up with the most!

Write in mirror language

Can you write a word in mirror writing, so that it looks right in a mirror?

For example, **Hello** would look like this: **olleH**

And **Pizza** would look like this: **azziP**

Then hold the book up to a mirror, and see if it worked!

Mirror drawing

Now see if you can do this!

Stand a small mirror here ...

And a box or book here, to block your view

Sit so that you can only see the mirror. Then try to copy the picture of the star, and draw another star next to it—only looking in the mirror! How hard is it?

Incredible illusions

Experiment with optical illusions ... and create your own!

The cafe wall

This famous illusion was first spotted on a real tiled wall in a cafe.

These tiles don't look so strange ... yet!

Just fill in every square with a dot in it in black, and things should change!

Shade every dotted square black, and see the illusion appear!

The pattern of slightly shifted black tiles fools your brain into thinking the lines are not flat. But they are!

Changing shades

Here's another brain-boggler. These blocks all look like the same shade, right?

Nothing to see here! Just lots of matching blocks.

Now, fill in the dotted boxes in solid black. The blocks look different!

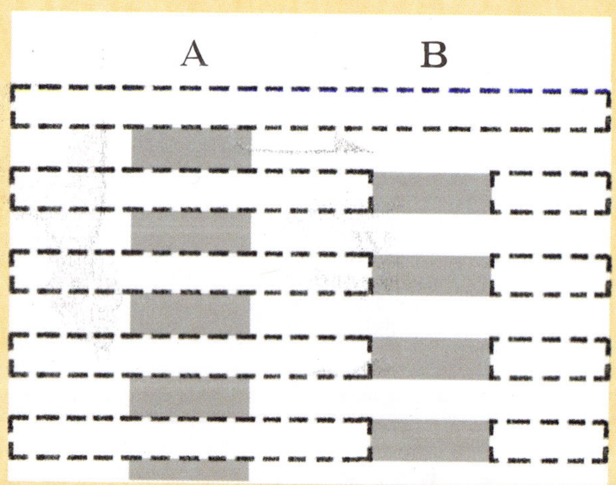

We decide how dark or light surfaces look by comparing them to what's around them.

The pattern of black strips confuses your brain into seeing different shades.

Yellow glow

And here's another!

Here are some shapes.

With a yellow pen, draw a thick line all around each shape, just inside the outline, like this.

It will make them seem to fill up with yellow ... even though they're still white inside!

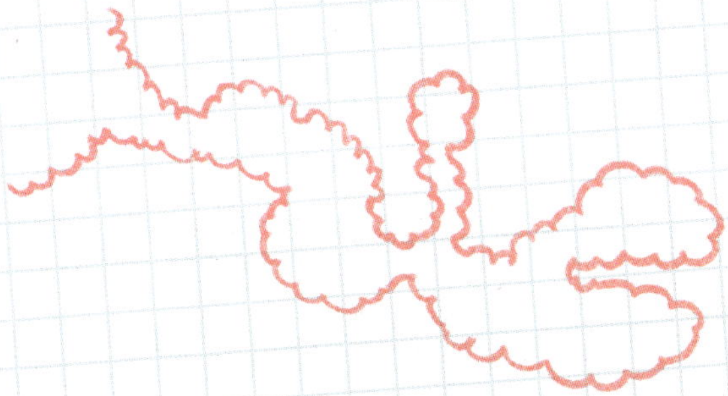

Super Stroop!

Have you ever heard of a stroop test? Here's one to try right now!

What do you see?

In a stroop test, you see a list of words. All you have to do is say what shade each one is. So if you see a blue word, say blue. Say all of them, and ask someone to time you to see how fast you can do it.

YELLOW	BLUE	RED	GREEN
PURPLE	PINK	ORANGE	BLUE
RED	GREEN	PINK	YELLOW

Now try this!

Here's another test, but it's a little harder.
Do the exact same thing again—say the shade you see.

PURPLE	ORANGE	PINK	YELLOW
GREEN	BLUE	RED	PINK
PURPLE	YELLOW	ORANGE	BLUE

Tricky, right? In fact, most people are MUCH slower on test 2!

But why?

This happens because once you learn to read, your brain quickly reads any word it sees. It's really hard to ignore the word and just look at the shade!

Design a Stroop!

There are other ways to do this test, too. For example, you could draw a set of different shapes and give them the wrong labels.

Or try groups of dots with the wrong numbers.

That's disgusting!

Ewwww! Yuck! You know when something's disgusting ... but how?

Would you eat a bug?

In some countries, it's normal to eat insects ... but in others, just the idea of it makes people go

"Ewwwwww!"

Crickets are a popular food around the world.

It's not that bugs are or are not gross. It's just what you're used to. If you see other people feeling disgusted by something, you'll probably start feeling the same way!

Naturally gross

Meanwhile, there are some things that EVERYONE finds gross—like poop! That's because it contains germs, so we have an instinct to avoid it.

Blue food

Even the way food looks can change how we feel about it. If we're used to pasta being white, it looks unappealing if it's bright blue!

Test it out!
Ask an adult to cook some pasta, and stir in some blue food dye.

Then put it on a plate.
Does the blueness put you off?

Gross or delicious?

Here are some dinners on plates.
Shade them in to make one look delicious and the other gross!

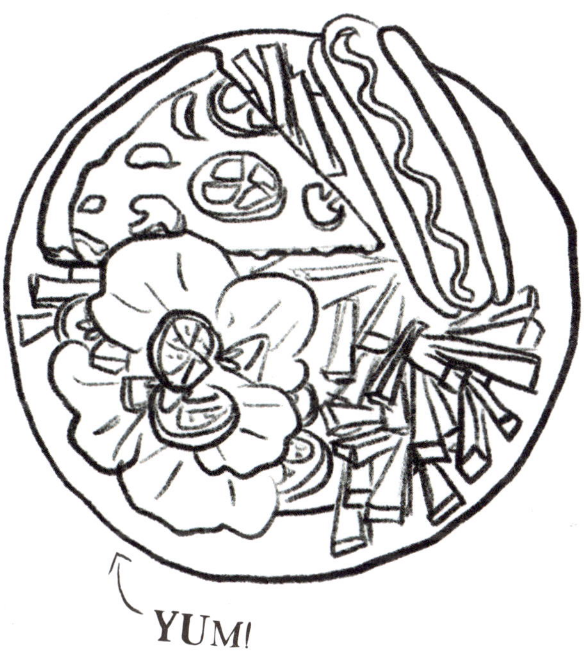

Answers

Page 8: Where is the Moon?

Page 15: Star science

Page 37: Draw a sound

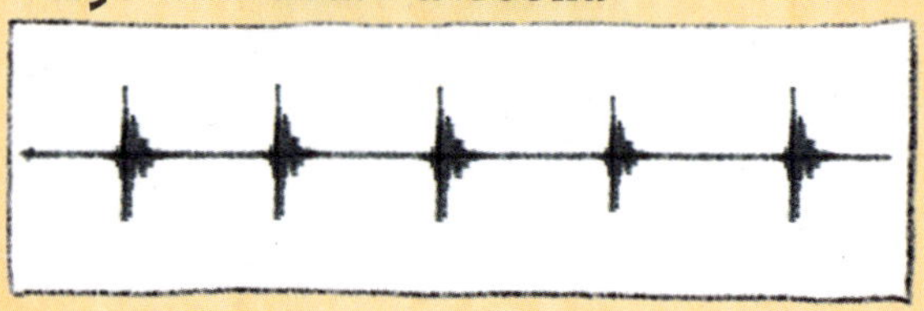

Page 41: Drawing atoms

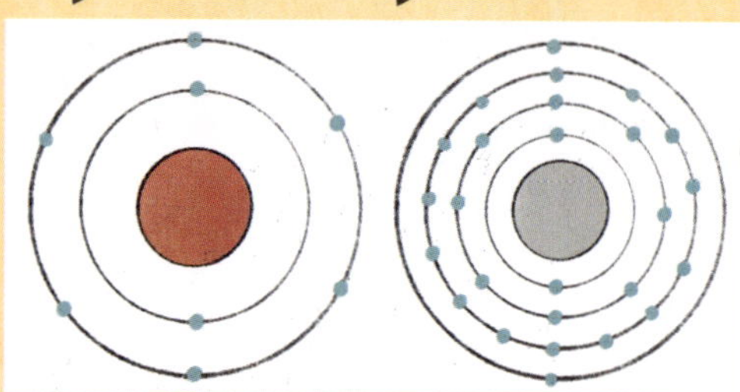

Page 53: Flood maps

Mr. Rainer's house is at risk of being flooded.

Page 57: Which is which?

Flu: Virus
Strep throat: Bacteria
Tuberculosis: Bacteria
Cholera: Bacteria
Covid-19: Virus
Food poisoning: Bacteria
Ebola: Virus

Page 61: Fossil finders

Page 69: Written in the rings

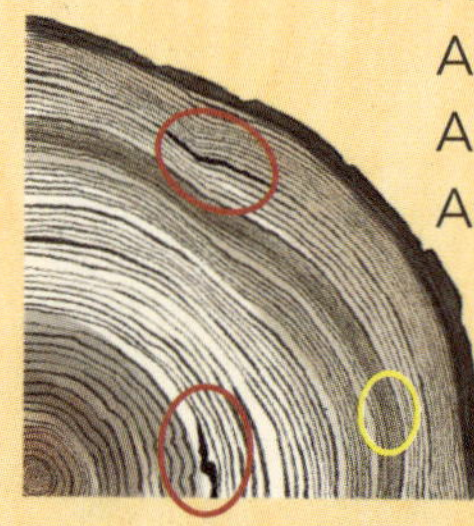

Answer: About 68 years old
Answer: Red rings on the picture
Answer: 12 years ago and 45 years ago
Answer: Yellow ring on the picture

Page 71: Migration maps

Page 73: Who eats who?

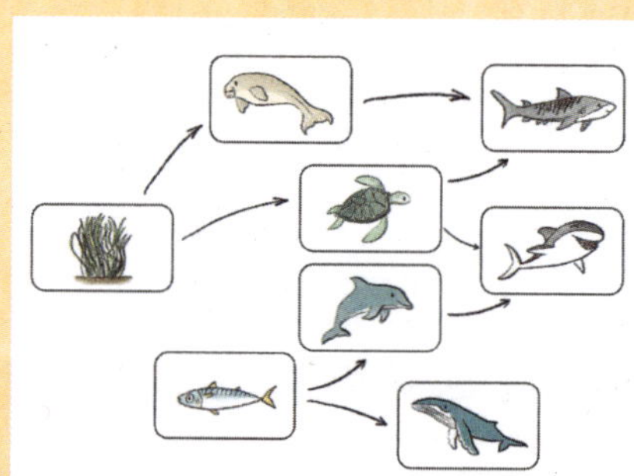

Glossary

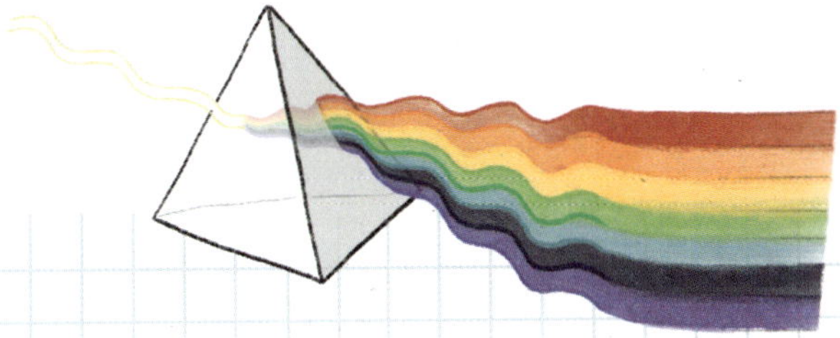

Ammonite A type of extinct sea creature, relates to octopuses, with a spiral shell.

Animation Using a sequence of pictures to make something appear to move.

Atoms The tiny units that materials are made of.

Bacteria Very small, single-celled microorganisms.

Balancing point A part of an object that it can balance on, with its weight spread evenly around that point.

Blind spot A part of the retina, at the back of the eyeball, that cannot sense light.

Camera obscura A dark room or box with a small hole to let in light, which creates an upside-down image opposite the hole.

Carbon A type of element, found in carbon dioxide and in many minerals, including graphite and diamond.

Cells The tiny building blocks that make up living things.

Carbon dioxide A type of gas found in the air, and released when fuel burn and when animals breathe.

Constellation A random arrangement of stars that can be seen as a pattern, shape our object.

Cyclone A swirling wind storm that forms over a warm ocean.

Density How heavy something is for its size.

Diamond A very hard, clear mineral made from the element carbon.

Digestive system The set of body organs that take in, break down and absorb food, and remove waste from it.

Ecosystem A habitat and the community of living things that are found there.

Electrons Tiny particles that move around in the outer layers of an atom

Electron shells Different orbits around the atom of an atom, which contain varying numbers of electrons.

Elements Basic, pure materials that are made of only one type of atom, such as gold and oxygen.

Energy The power to make things happen or do work.

Evaporate To change from a liquid into a gas.

Food chain A sequence of living things in which each one is eaten by the next.

Food web A network of plants and animals in an ecosystem that depend on each other for food.

Fossil The remains or trace of a prehistoric living thing, preserved in rock.

Friction A force that slows objects down as they rub or grip against each other.

Gas A substance with no fixed shape, in which molecules are far apart and move very fast.

Germs Tiny living things that can cause diseases in other living things.

Gravity A pulling force that makes objects attract other objects towards them.

Habitat The natural home or surroundings of a living thing.

Instinct An ability that an animal has automatically, without having to learn it, such as birds building nests.

Intestines Tubes inside the body that extract useful chemicals from food and collect waste.

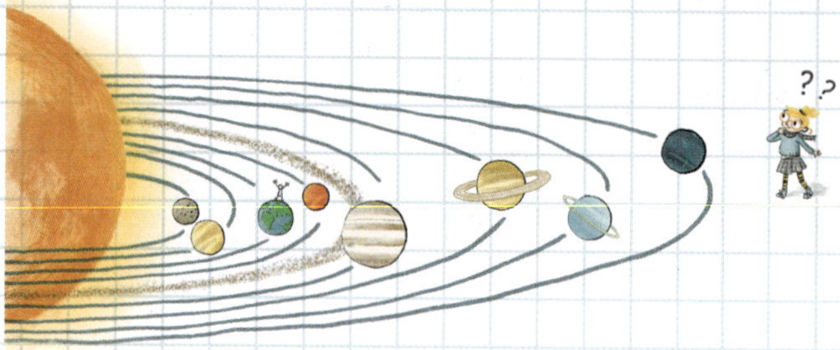

Invertebrate An animal without a backbone, such as a worm, octopus or butterfly.

Magnet A material or object that has a pulling force on some types of metal, or other magnets.

Meteorology The science or study of weather and the atmosphere.

Microscope A device that helps very small objects look bigger, making them easier to see and study.

Migration A long-distance journey made by animals to help them find food, keep warm or find a mate.

Mineral A pure, natural, non-living substance, such as iron, quartz or salt.

Molecules Units that materials are made of, made from atoms joined together.

Neurons Cells found in the brain and nerves that carry signals around the brain and body.

Nucleus The central part of an atom.

Optical illusion A picture that fools the brain into seeing something that isn't there, or seeing something differently from how it really is.

Orbit To circle around another object, such as the Moon orbiting around the Earth.

Oxygen A common gas that makes up part of the air, and that humans need to breathe.

Pitch How high or low a sound is.

Planet A ball of rock, liquid or gas (or a mixture), orbiting a star, such as the Sun.

Pollen Yellow powder released from flowers, containing male plant cells that are needed to make seeds.

Porous Containing tiny holes or spaces, and able to soak up water.

Precipitation Water that falls from the atmosphere to the ground, such as rain, snow or hail.

Reproduce Living things reproduce when they make copies of themselves, for example by having babies or dividing in two.

Retina An area at the back of the eye containing special cells that can detect light.

Rhythm A regular, repeated pattern of beats found in most types of music.

Rock A mixed substance made of two or more minerals.

Single-celled Having only one cell.

Solar System Our Sun and the planets and other space objects that orbit around it.

Sound waves Pressure waves that spread out through the air from an object that is making a sound.

Species The scientific name for a particular type of living thing.

Telescope A device that can make faraway objects appear bigger and closer, making them easier to see.

Thermometer A dive that measures temperature .

Tsunami A powerful, fast wave created when a large amount of water moves suddenly, , for example when there's an earthquake on the seabed.

Vertebrate An animal with a backbone, such as a fish, horse or human.

Vibrate To shake quickly to and fro.

Virus A type of very small germ that can invade living cells and use them to make copies of itself. Some viruses cause diseases.

Waveform A way of representing a sound as a pattern on a graph.

Wavelength The length of a wave, from the top of one wave to the top of the next.